BOOKS BY OGDEN NASH

*I'm a Stranger Here Myself*

*Good Intentions*

*Many Long Years Ago*

*Versus*

*Family Reunion*

*Parents Keep Out: Elderly Poems for Youngerly Readers*

# Parents
## Keep Out

# OGDEN NASH

# *Parents Keep Out*

## ELDERLY POEMS FOR YOUNGERLY READERS

DRAWINGS BY BARBARA CORRIGAN

*Boston*

LITTLE, BROWN AND COMPANY

1951

*Published simultaneously
in Canada by McClelland and Stewart Limited*

PRINTED IN THE UNITED STATES OF AMERICA

Since parents can't keep out of anything, I resignedly address these words to them. Many parents will find that they have read some of the verses in previous books of mine. I shall not apologize. Anybody who has read previous books of mine is a trespasser in this one, which has been compiled for a younger generation. I do not regard it as a children's book, however; I simply hope it is a book that anyone born less than fourteen or fifteen years ago may enjoy. I have written a lot of verses about children, but they are of no interest to children, as they were written for parents; on the other hand I have been pleased to discover that some of the pieces dealing with the aberrations and anomalies of the adult world have found favor here and there among the kids. This makes me very proud; indeed at such times I feel like the cryptographer who has cracked the code, or the first man to reach the moon, because, in my experience, full communication between the generations simply doesn't exist. There is a curtain between the mind of the child and the mind of the parent as opaque as any between the mind of the Occidental and the mind of the Russian or the Chinese. Words may be interchanged, but they do not mean the same thing to one as to the other; the language is purely diplomatic — or undiplomatic — and the final understanding is about equal to that achieved by diplomats. Of course it may be that if the kids do like any of these verses it is for the very reason that the Kremlin is gratified by any sign of the collapse of capitalism; watchful young eyes may here perceive indications of the breakup of the old people's world. Nevertheless, flushed by a few minor successes among my juniors, I have risked hastening the revolution by gathering for them from my past this potpourri of foolish jokes, anecdotes, fables, and other trivia, embellished with rhymes and conclusions both true and false. Perhaps for the very reason that this particular collection is not calculated, dear parents who have not kept out, to present us as the omniscient and infallible paragons they think we think we are, it may persuade our young to treat us more gently when they take over. God willing, it may even persuade a disreputable handful that they are as silly as we.

O. N.

# CONTENTS

[ xi ]

[ xiii ]

*Parents*
*Keep Out*

*ASK DADDY, HE WON'T KNOW*

Now that they've abolished chrome work
I'd like to call their attention to home work.
Here it is only three decades since my scholarship was
famous,
And I'm an ignoramus.
I cannot think which goes sideways and which goes up and
down, a parallel or a meridian,
Nor do I know the name of him who first translated the
Bible into Indian, I see him only as an enterprising
colonial Gideon.
I have difficulty with dates,
To say nothing of the annual rainfall of the Southern Cen-
tral States,
And the only way I can distinguish proper from improper
fractions

[ 3 ]

Is by their actions.

Naturally the correct answers are just back of the tip of my tongue,

But try to explain that to your young.

I am overwhelmed by their erudite banter,

I am in no condition to differentiate between Tamerlane and Tam o' Shanter.

I reel, I sway, I am utterly exhausted;

Should you ask me when Chicago was founded I could only reply I didn't even know it was losted.


## A BEGINNER'S GUIDE TO THE OCEAN

Let us now consider the ocean.

It is always in motion.

It is generally understood to be the source of much of our rain,

And ten thousand fleets are said to have swept over it in vain.

When the poet requested it to break break break on its cold gray rocks it obligingly broke broke broke,

Which as the poet was Alfred Lord Tennyson didn't surprise him at all but if it had been me I would probably have had a stroke.

There is an immortal dignity about something like the Atlantic,

Which seems to drive unimmortal undignified human beings frustratedly frantic.

Just give them one foot on the beach and people who were perfectly normal formerly, or whilom,

Why, they are subject to whoops and capers that would
    get them blackballed from an asylum;
Yet be they never so rampant and hollerant,
The ocean is tolerant,
Except a couple of times a day it gives up in disgust and
    goes off by itself and hides,
And that, my dears, accounts for the tides.


## PROCRASTINATION IS ALL OF THE TIME

Torpor and sloth, torpor and sloth,
These are the cooks that unseason the broth.
Slothor and torp, slothor and torp
The directest of bee-line ambitions can warp.
He who is slothic, he who is torporal,
Will not be promoted to sergeant or corporal.
No torporer drowsy, no comatose slother
Will make a good banker, not even an author.
Torpor I deprecate, sloth I deplore,
Torpor is tedious, sloth is a bore.
Sloth is a bore, and torpor is tedious,
Fifty parts comatose, fifty tragedious.
How drear, on a planet redundant with woes,
That sloth is not slumber, nor torpor repose.
That the innocent joy of not getting things done
Simmers sulkily down to plain not having fun.
You smile in the morn like a bride in her bridalness
At the thought of a day of nothing but idleness.
By midday you're slipping, by evening a lunatic,
A perusing-the-newspapers-all-afternoonatic,
Worn to a wraith from the half-hourly jaunt

[ 5 ]

After glasses of water you didn't want,
And at last when onto your pallet you creep,
You discover yourself too tired to sleep.
O torpor and sloth, torpor and sloth,
These are the cooks that unseason the broth.
Torpor is harrowing, sloth it is irksome —
Everyone ready? Let's go out and worksome.


## EVERYBODY HAS AN UNCLE

I wish I were a Tibetan monk
Living in a monastery.
I would unpack my trunk
And store it in a tronastery;
I would collect all my junk
And send it to a jonastery;
I would try to reform an unc-
le and pay his expenses at an onastery,
And if my income shrunk
I would send it to a shronastery.


## CELERY

Celery, raw,
Develops the jaw,
But celery, stewed,
Is more quietly chewed.

Rainy vacations
Try people's patience.
To expect rain in the autumn
Experience has tautumn,
And rain in the spring and winter
Makes no stories for the printer,
But rain on summer colonies
Breeds misdemeanors and felonies.
Summer cottages are meant just to sleep in,
Not to huddle all day in a heap in,
And whether at sea level or in higher places
There are not enough fireplaces,
And the bookcase stares at you starkly
And seems to be full of nothing but Volume II of the life
    of Rutherford B. Hayes, and *The Rosary*, by Florence
    M. Barclay,
And everybody wishes they had brought woolens and
    tweeds instead of linens and foulards,
And if you succeed in lining up four for bridge the only
    deck turns out to have only fifty-one cards,
And tennis rackets grow frazzled and golf sticks rusty and
    bathing suits moldy,
And parents grow scoldly,
And on all sides you hear nothing but raindrops going
    sputter-sput, sputter-sput,
And bureau drawers won't open and bathroom doors won't
    shut,
And all attempts at amusement fail,
Even reading the previous tenants' jettisoned mail,
Although naturally it would never have been jettisoned

If it hadn't been reticent.
But you could stand everything if it wasn't for one malignant committee,
Which is the one that turns the sun on again just as you are leaving for the city.
Yes indeed, rainy vacations
Certainly try people's patience.

## PLEASE PASS THE BISCUIT

I have a little dog,
Her name is Spangle.
And when she eats
I think she'll strangle.

She's darker than Hamlet,
Lighter than Porgy;
Her heart is gold,
Her odor, dorgy.

Her claws click-click
Across the floor,
Her nose is always
Against a door.

The squirrel flies
Her pursuing mouth;
Should he fly north,
She pursues him south.

Yet do not mock her
As she hunts;
Remember, she caught
A milkman once.

Like liquid gems
Her eyes burn clearly;
She's five years old,
And house-trained, nearly.

Her shame is deep
When she has erred;
She dreads the blow
Less than the word.

I marvel that such
Small ribs as these
Can cage such vast
Desire to please.

She's as much a part
Of the house as the mortgage,
Spangle, I wish you
A ripe old dortgage.

## DON'T CRY, DARLING, IT'S BLOOD
## ALL RIGHT

Whenever poets want to give you the idea that something
is particularly meek and mild,
They compare it to a child,
Thereby proving that though poets with poetry may be
rife
They don't know the facts of life.
If of compassion you desire either a tittle or a jot,
Don't try to get it from a tot.
Hard-boiled, sophisticated adults like me and you
May enjoy ourselves thoroughly with *Little Women* and
*Winnie-the-Pooh*,
But innocent infants these titles from their reading course
eliminate
As soon as they discover that it was honey and nuts and
mashed potatoes instead of human flesh that Winnie-
the-Pooh and Little Women ate.
Innocent infants have no use for fables about rabbits or
donkeys or tortoises or porpoises,

What they want is something with plenty of well-
     mutilated corpoises.
Not on legends of how the rose came to be a rose instead
     of a petunia is their fancy fed,
But on the inside story of how somebody's bones got
     ground up to make somebody else's bread.
They'll go to sleep listening to the story of the little
     beggarmaid who got to be queen by being kind to
     the bees and the birds,
But they're all eyes and ears the minute they suspect a
     wolf or a giant is going to tear some poor wood-
     cutter into quarters or thirds.
It really doesn't take much to fill their cup;
All they want is for somebody to be eaten up.
Therefore I say unto you, all you poets who are so crazy
     about meek and mild little children and their an-
     gelic air,
If you are sincere and really want to please them, why
     just go out and get yourselves devoured by a bear.

### THE PORCUPINE

Any hound a porcupine nudges
Can't be blamed for harboring grudges.
I know one hound that laughed all winter
At a porcupine that sat on a splinter.

### THE PANTHER

The panther is like a leopard,
Except it hasn't been peppered.
Should you behold a panther crouch,

Prepare to say Ouch.
Better yet, if called by a panther,
Don't anther.


## THE CALF

Pray, butcher, spare yon tender calf!
Accept my plea on his behalf;
He's but a babe, too young by far
To perish in the abattoir.
Oh, cruel butcher, let him feed
And gambol on the verdant mead;
Let clover tops and grassy banks
Fill out those childish ribs and flanks.
Then may we, at some future meal,
Pitch into beef, instead of veal.


## VERY LIKE A WHALE

One thing that literature would be greatly the better for
Would be a more restricted employment by authors of
simile and metaphor.
Authors of all races, be they Greeks, Romans, Teutons or
Celts,
Can't seem just to say that anything is the thing it is but
have to go out of their way to say that it is like some-
thing else.
What does it mean when we are told
That the Assyrian came down like a wolf on the fold?

In the first place, George Gordon Byron had had enough
experience
To know that it probably wasn't just one Assyrian, it was
a lot of Assyrians.
However, as too many arguments are apt to induce apo-
plexy and thus hinder longevity,
We'll let it pass as one Assyrian for the sake of brevity.
Now then, this particular Assyrian, the one whose cohorts
were gleaming in purple and gold,
Just what does the poet mean when he says he came down
like a wolf on the fold?
In heaven and earth more than is dreamed of in our phi-
losophy there are a great many things,
But I don't imagine that among them there is a wolf with
purple and gold cohorts or purple and gold anythings.
No, no, Lord Byron, before I'll believe that this Assyrian
was actually like a wolf I must have some kind of
proof;
Did he run on all fours and did he have a hairy tail and
a big red mouth and big white teeth and did he say
Woof woof?
Frankly I think it very unlikely, and all you were entitled
to say, at the very most,
Was that the Assyrian cohorts came down like a lot of
Assyrian cohorts about to destroy the Hebrew host.
But that wasn't fancy enough for Lord Byron, oh dear me
no, he had to invent a lot of figures of speech and
then interpolate them,
With the result that whenever you mention Old Testament
soldiers to people they say Oh yes, they're the ones
that a lot of wolves dressed up in gold and purple
ate them.

That's the kind of thing that's being done all the time by
    poets, from Homer to Tennyson;
They're always comparing ladies to lilies and veal to venison,
And they always say things like that the snow is a white
    blanket after a winter storm.
Oh it is, is it, all right then, you sleep under a six-inch
    blanket of snow and I'll sleep under a half-inch blanket
    of unpoetical blanket material and we'll see which
    one keeps warm,
And after that maybe you'll begin to comprehend dimly
What I mean by too much metaphor and simile.


## THE JELLYFISH

Who wants my jellyfish?
I'm not sellyfish!


## ABDICATION OF A JESTER

Once there was a man and he wasn't famous for his clothes,
He was famous for his *bons mots*.
Dinner parties waited hungrily if he didn't come in till late
Because they could count on him to scintillate;
Just give him a cocktail or two to relax him
And you would be repaid with an epigram or a maxim;
He was invariably original,
And he did not have to depend for his effect on the indeli-
    cate or sacrileginal;
Of quips and anecdotes he was a warehouse,
And everybody wanted him at their house.

Yes indeed, he was quite a wit,
And then one day he suddenly quit.
He seldom went out and when he did go out he seldom
opened his mouth,
And when he did, it was only to remark on the current
blizzard or flood or drouth;
On scintillation he clamped down a total embargo,
And his most stimulating remark to a dinner partner in
three months was, So you're from Louisville, I used
to know some people named Perkins in Louisville, but
it seems to me I heard they'd moved to Chicago.
And at first everybody was patient but at last their brows
grew darkling,
And they went to him and said, Look here, how about a
little sparkling?
And he said, Do you see these lips?
And they said they did, and he said, Well they shall never
more be crossed by wanton wiles and cranks and quips.
He said, I have spent my life studying the fundamentals
of wit and humor and table talk,
I have spent a fortune in time and effort to master the art
of stimulating and able talk;
To every aphorism of mine you ever quoted,
Why, years of experience were devoted,
And then, he said, and then the baby is told to speak to
Mr. Katz the grocer on the telephone, Go ahead, baby,
speak to Mr. Katz, and the baby says Meow,
And the spasms of mirth raised by baby's repartee still echo
in my ears right now.
No, he said, hereafter count me not a wit, count me simply
a good neighbor.
I am too old and proud to compete with unskilled labor.

In far Tibet
There live a lama,
He got no poppa,
Got no momma,

He got no wife,
He got no chillun,
Got no use
For penicillun,

He got no soap,
He got no opera,
He don't know Irium
From copra,

He got no songs,
He got no banter,
Don't know Crosby,
Don't know Cantor,

He got no teeth,
He got no gums,
Don't eat no Spam,
Don't need no Tums.

He love to nick him
When he shave;
He also got
No hair to save.

Got no distinction,
No clear head,
Don't call for Calvert;
Drink milk instead.

He use no lotions
For allurance,
He got no car
And no insurance,

He live just like
The lower mammals,
Got no sore throat
From not smoking Camels.

No Winchell warnings,
No Pearson rumor
For this self-centered
Nonconsumer.

Indeed, the
Ignorant Have-Not
Don't even know
What he don't got.

If you will mind
The box-tops, comma,
I think I'll go
And join that lama.

## ELECTRA BECOMES MORBID

### I

Abandon for a moment, friends,
Your frivolous means, your futile ends;
Life is not wholly beer and skittles,
A treasure hunt for love and victuals;
And so at times I think we ought
To pause and think a sobering thought.
Myself, I feel a dark despair
When I consider human hair.
I'm chicken-hearted, beetle-browed,
As I behold the heedless crowd,
Knowing each carefree individual
The slave of hair that runs on schidual.

On every human head or chin
It's falling out or growing in.
Yon whistling adolescent scholar,
Released from Ye Olde Tonsorial Parlor,
Runs up his neck with fingers tense
Like sticks along a picket fence.
His scalp is all Bay Rum and bristles,
Therefore he's pleased and therefore whistles.
Yea, he rejoices, quite unknowing
That all the time his hair is growing.
O woe is you, unhappy scholar,
Next month you'll be back in the tonsorial parlor.

II

Myself I feel a dark despair,
When I consider human hair,
(Fine filaments sprouting from the skin),
I tremble like an aspirin.
For men and women everywhere
Unconsciously are growing hair,
Or, if the other hand you choose,
With every breath a hair they lose.
Unbid it cometh, likewise goeth,
And oftentimes it's doing boeth.
This habit is the chief determinant
Why permanent waves are less than permanent.
You rise, Madame, you face your mirror,
You utter cries of shame and terror.
What though to males you look all right?
For heaven's sake, your hair's a sight.
You hasten to the Gallic lair
Where lurks Maurice, or Jean or Pierre.

Between arrival and departure
You suffer hours of vicious torture,
At last emerging, white and weak,
But sure at least your mane is chic.
Thus you rejoice, my dear, unknowing
That all the time your hair is growing.
The waves so dearly purchasèd
Next month will have grown a foot or so away from your
    head.

### III

I've said, I think, I think we ought
To think at times a sobering thought.
Man's lot it is to be a field
For crops that no nutrition yield,
That filter through his tender skin
And ripen on his head or chin.
I face mankind and shudder, knowing
That everybody's hair is growing;
That lovers, linked in darkened hallways,
Are capped with hair that groweth always;
That millions, shaven in the morning,
At eve find beards their jowls adorning;
That hair is creeping through the scalps
Of yodelers yodeling in the Alps,
And pushing through the epidermises
Of peasants frolicking at kermises;
And poking bravely through the pores
Of cannibals on tropic shores;
That freezing, scorching, raining, snowing,
People's hair is always growing.
I contemplate with dark despair

The awful force of growing hair,
Although admitting, to be quite honest,
That it will be worth a million Niagaras to humanity if
    Science can ever get it harnessed.

## TARKINGTON, THOU SHOULD'ST BE LIVING IN THIS HOUR

O Adolescence, O Adolescence,
I wince before thine incandescence.
Thy constitution young and hearty
Is too much for this aged party.
Thou standest with loafer-flattened feet
Where bras and funny papers meet.
When anxious elders swarm about
Crying "Where are you going?" thou answerest "Out,"
Leaving thy parents swamped in debts
For bubble gum and cigarettes.

Thou spurnest in no uncertain tone
The sirloin for the ice-cream cone;
Not milk, but cola, is thy potion;
Thou wearest earrings in the ocean,
Blue jeans at dinner, or maybe shorts,
And lipstick on the tennis courts.

Forever thou whisperest, two by two,
Of who is madly in love with who.
The car thou needest every day,
Let hub caps scatter where they may.
For it would start unfriendly talk
If friends should chance to see thee walk.

Friends! Heavens, how they come and go!
Best pal today, tomorrow foe,
Since to distinguish thou dost fail
Twixt confidante and tattletale,
And blanchest to find the beach at noon
With sacred midnight secrets strewn.

Strewn! All is lost and nothing found.
Lord, how thou leavest things around!
Sweaters and rackets in the stable,
And purse upon the drugstore table,
And cameras rusting in the rain,
And Daddy's patience down the drain.

Ah well, I must not carp and cavil,
I'll chew the spinach, spit out the gravel,
Remembering how my heart has leapt
At times when me thou didst accept.
Still, I'd like to be present, I must confess,
When thine own adolescents adolesce.

## NO DOCTORS TODAY, THANK YOU

They tell me that euphoria is the feeling of feeling wonder-
ful, well, today I feel euphorian,
Today I have the agility of a Greek god and the appetite
of a Victorian.
Yes, today I may even go forth without my galoshes,
Today I am a swashbuckler, would anybody like me to
buckle any swashes?
This is my euphorian day,
I will ring welkins and before anybody answers I will run
away.

I will tame me a caribou
And bedeck it with maribou.
I will pen me my memoirs.
Ah youth, youth! What euphorian days them was!
I wasn't much of a hand for the boudoirs,
I was generally to be found where the food was.
Does anybody want any flotsam?
I've gotsam.
Does anybody want any jetsam?
I can getsam.
I can play chopsticks on the Wurlitzer,
I can speak Portuguese like a Berlitzer.
I can don or doff my shoes without tying or untying the
      laces because I am wearing moccasins,
And I practically know the difference between serums and
      antitoccasins.
Kind people, don't think me purse-proud, don't set me
      down as vainglorious,
I'm just a little euphorious.


## FRAGONARD

There was an old miser named Clarence,
Who simonized both of his parents.
"The initial expense,"
He remarked, "is immense,
But I'll save it on wearance and tearance."

Once there was a poem, and it wasn't by Edgar A. Guest,
And it said children ought to agree like little birdies in
  their nest.
Oh forsooth forsooth!
That poem was certainly more poetry than truth,
Because do you believe that little birdies in their nest agree?
It doesn't sound very probable to me.
Ah no, but I can tell you what does sound probable,
And that is that life in a nest is just one long quarrel and
  squabbable.
Look at that young mother robin over in that elm, or is
  it a beech,
She has two little robins and she thinks she has solved her
  problem because she has learned not to bring home
  just one worm but a worm for each.
She is very pleased with her understanding of fledgling
  psychology, but in just about two minutes she is going
  to lose a year's growth,
Because she's going to find that one little robin gets no
  worms and the other robin gets both,
And if one little robin gets out of the nest on the wrong
  side and nothing can please it,
Why the other little robin will choose that moment to
  tease it,
And if one little robin starts a game the other little robin
  will stop it,
And if one little robin builds a castle the other little robin
  will knock it down and if one little robin blows a
  bubble the other little robin will pop it.
Yes, I bet that if you walked up to any nest and got a good
  revealing glimpse,

Why, you would find that our little feathered friendlets
    disagree just like human imps,
And I also bet that their distracted feathered parents quote
    feathered poetry to them by whoever the most popular
    feathered poet may be,
All about why don't they like little children in their
    nurseries agree.
Well, to put the truth about youth in a very few words,
Why the truth is that little birds do agree like children
    and children do agree like little birds,
Because you take offspring, and I don't care whether a
    house or a tree is their abode,
They may love each other but they aren't going to agree
    with each other anywhere except in an ode.
It doesn't seem to have occurred to the poet,
That nobody agrees with anybody else anyhow, but adults
    conceal it and infants show it.


## THE PARSNIP

The parsnip, children, I repeat,
Is simply an anemic beet.
Some people call the parsnip edible;
Myself, I find this claim incredible.


## ASSORTED CHOCOLATES

If some confectioner were willing
To let the shape announce the filling,
We'd encounter fewer assorted chocs,
Bitten into and returned to the box.

The hunter crouches in his blind
'Neath camouflage of every kind,
And conjures up a quacking noise
To lend allure to his decoys.
This grown-up man, with pluck and luck,
Is hoping to outwit a duck.

## ALLERGY IN A COUNTRY CHURCHYARD

Once there was a man named Mr. Weaver,
And he had a lot of hay but he didn't have any hay fever,
So he ran an advertisement which he wanted to charge, but
for which he was compelled to pay,
And he advertised that he would like to meet up with
somebody who had a lot of hay fever but didn't have
any hay,
So along came a man and he said he had seen his ad in
the paper,
And was the proposition serious or merely a prankish caper,
And Mr. Weaver said it was as serious as the dickens,
Because to his mind hay fever was to the human race what
bumblefoot, limber neck and edema of the wattles
were to chickens,
And he said he was the most modest of men,
But never having had hay fever he felt very irked at being
outexperienced by any passing bumblefooted hen,
And the man said I can describe hay fever for you so you'll
know all about it but first how much are you prepared
to pay?

And Mr. Weaver said, "Can I charge it?" and the man said
No, so Mr. Weaver said he would give him all his hay,
So the man said All right and threw pepper in Mr. Weaver's
eyes,
And Mr. Weaver said, "What are you doing?" and the
man said "Never mind, just kindly answer the following questions with the correct replies,
What's the kind of nut you put back in the dish at cocktail parties," and Mr. Weaver said "A cashew," and
the man said *Gesundheit.* What material do politi-
cians say their opponents' lies are composed of?" and
Mr. Weaver said "The whole cloth," and the man
said "No no try again," and Mr. Weaver said "A tissue,"
and the man said *Gesundheit.* What's a filmy collar
often worn by women?" and Mr. Weaver said "A
fichu," and the man said *Gesundheit.* Now you know
all about hay fever,"
So he went off with Mr. Weaver's hay, but first he tele-
phoned an old schoolmate in Vancouver and charged
the call to Mr. Weaver.

### COMPLAINT TO FOUR ANGELS

Every night at sleepy-time
Into bed I gladly climb.
Every night anew I hope
That with the covers I can cope.

Adjust the blanket fore and aft,
Swallow next a soothing draught;
Then a page of Scott or Cooper
May induce a healthful stupor.

O the soft luxurious dark;
Even dogs forget to bark.
Traffic dies along the street.
The light is out. So are your feet.

Adjust the blanket aft and fore,
Sigh, and settle down once more.
Behold, a breeze! The curtains puff.
One blanket isn't quite enough.

Yawn and rise and seek your slippers,
Which, by now, are cold as kippers.
Yawn, and stretch, and prod yourself,
And fetch a blanket from the shelf.

And so to bed again, again,
Cozy under blankets twain.
Welcome warmth and sweet nirvana
Till eight o'clock or so mañana.

You sleep as deep as Keats or Bacon;
Then you dream and toss and waken.
Where is the breeze? There isn't any.
Two blankets, boy, are one too many.

O stilly night, why are you not
Consistent in your cold and hot?
O slumber's chains, unlocked so oft
With blankets being donned or doffed!

The angels who should guard my bed
I fear are slumbering instead.
O angels, please resume your hovering;
I'll sleep, and you adjust the covering.

## THE ANT

The ant has made himself illustrious
Through constant industry industrious.
So what?
Would you be calm and placid
If you were full of formic acid?

## THE HIPPOPOTAMUS

Behold the hippopotamus!
We laugh at how he looks to us,
And yet in moments dank and grim
I wonder how we look to him.
Peace, peace, thou hippopotamus!
We really look all right to us,
As you no doubt delight the eye
Of other hippopotami.

## THE CENTIPEDE

I objurgate the centipede,
A bug we do not really need.
At sleepy-time he beats a path
Straight to the bedroom or the bath.
You always wallop where he's not,
Or, if he is, he makes a spot.

## THE SNIFFLE

In spite of her sniffle,
Isabel's chiffle.
Some girls with a sniffle
Would be weepy and tiffle;
They would look awful,
Like a rained-on waffle,
But Isabel's chiffle
In spite of her sniffle.
Her nose is more red
With a cold in her head,

But then, to be sure,
Her eyes are bluer.
Some girls with a snuffle,
Their tempers are uffle,
But when Isabel's snivelly
She's snivelly civilly,
And when she is snuffly
She's perfectly luffly.


## TABLEAU AT TWILIGHT

I sit in the dusk. I am all alone.
Enter a child and an ice-cream cone.

A parent is easily beguiled
By sight of this coniferous child.

The friendly embers warmer gleam,
The cone begins to drip ice cream.

Cones are composed of many a vitamin.
My lap is not the place to bitamin.

Although my raiment is not chinchilla,
I flinch to see it become vanilla.

Coniferous child, when vanilla melts
I'd rather it melted somewhere else.

Exit child with remains of cone.
I sit in the dusk. I am all alone,

Muttering spells like an angry Druid,
Alone, in the dusk, with the cleaning fluid.

## MAN BITES DOG–DAYS

In this fairly temperate clime
Summertime is itchy time.
O'er rocks and stumps and ruined walls
Shiny poison ivy crawls.
Every walk in woods and fields
Its aftermath of itching yields.
Hand me down my rusty hatchet;
Someone murmured, Do not scratch it.

Reason permeates my rhyme:
Summertime is itchy time.
Beneath the orange August moon
Overfed mosquitoes croon.
After sun-up, flies and midges

Raise on people bumps and ridges.
Hand me down my rusty hatchet;
Someone murmured, Do not scratch it.

Lo, the year is in its prime;
Summertime is itchy time.
People loll upon the beaches
Ripening like gaudy peaches.
Friends, the beach is not the orchard,
Nor is the peach by sunburn tortured.
Hand me down my rusty hatchet;
Someone murmured, Do not scratch it.

Now the menu is sublime;
Summertime is itchy time.
Berries, clams, and lobsters tease
Our individual allergies.
Rash in rosy splendor thrives,
Running neck-and-neck with hives.
Hand me down my rusty hatchet;
Someone murmured, Do not scratch it.

The bluebells and the cowbells chime;
Summertime is itchy time.
Despite cold soup, and ice, and Thermoses,
Garments cling to epidermises.
That fiery-footed centipede,
Prickly heat prowls forth to feed.
Hand me down my rusty hatchet;
Someone murmured, Do not scratch it.

Hatchet-killings ain't a crime:
Summertime is itchy time.

## THE DUCK

Behold the duck.
It does not cluck.
A cluck it lacks.
It quacks.
It is specially fond
Of a puddle or pond.
When it dines or sups,
It bottoms ups.


## THE CANARY

The song of canaries
Never varies,
And when they're moulting
They're pretty revolting.


## THE LAMA

The one-l lama,
He's a priest.
The two-l llama,
He's a beast.
And I will bet
A silk pajama
There isn't any
Three-l lllama.*

* The author's attention has been called to a type of conflagration known as a three-alarmer. Pooh.

## I'M TERRIBLY SORRY FOR YOU, BUT I CAN'T HELP LAUGHING

Everybody has a perfect right to do what they please,
But one thing that I advise everybody not to do is to contract
    a laughable disease.
There is something impressive about cholera,
And anybody who undergoes an operation gets a repu-
    tation for courage even if they are a screaming
    cowardly hollera;
People speak of you respectfully if you catch bubonic,
And if you get typhus they think you have done some-
    thing positively mastodonic;
One touch of leprosy makes the whole world your kin,
And even a slight concussion earns you an anxious inquiry
    and not a leering grin.
Yes, as long as people are pretty sure you have something
    you are going to be removed by,
Why they are very sympathetic, and books and flowers and
    visits and letters are what their sympathy is proved by.
But unfortunately there are other afflictions anatomical,
And people insist on thinking that a lot of them are comical,
And if you are afflicted with this kind of affliction people
    are amused and disdainful,

Because they are not bright enough to realize that an affliction can be ludicrous and still be ominous and painful.
Suppose for instance you have a dreadful attack of jaundice,
 what do they do?
They come around and smile and say Well well, how are
 you today, Dr. Fu-Manchu?
The early martyrs thought they knew what it was to be
 taken over the jumps,
But no martyr really ought to get his diploma until he
 has undergone his friends' witticisms during his
 mumps.
When you have laryngitis they rejoice,
Because apparently the funniest thing in the world is when
 you can't curse and swear at them for laughing at your
 lost voice, because you have lost your voice.
Toothache is another diversion that hearty amusement
 yields,
And if you have a severe enough case of sunburn they find
 you funnier than W. C. Fields.
So I advise you, at the risk of being pedantic,
If you must be sick, by all means choose a sickness that is
 preferably fatal and certainly romantic,
Because it is much better to have that kind of sickness and
 be sick unto death or anyway half to death,
Than to have the other kind and be laughed to death.


### THE STRANGE CASE OF MR. FORTAGUE'S
### DISAPPOINTMENT

Once upon a time there was a man named Mr. Lionel
 Fortague.
He didn't have very much to talk about.

In summer he used to ask people if it was hot enough for them.

It always was.

In winter he used to ask people if it was cold enough for them.

It always was.

Mr. Lionel Fortague got pretty sick of people it was hot enough for.

He got pretty sick of people it was cold enough for, too.

He decided he would arise and go now.

He decided he would go to Innisfree.

The people of Innisfree are different, thought Mr. Lionel Fortague.

As soon as he got to Innisfree he asked the people if it was cold enough for them.

They asked him What? Was what cold enough for who?

Mr. Lionel Fortague was delighted.

I knew Innisfree would be different, he said to himself.

He could hardly wait for summer to verify his conclusion.

As soon as summer came he asked everybody if it was hot enough for them.

Everybody said the question was familiar but they couldn't remember the answer.

Mr. Lionel Fortague said he would settle down on Innisfree, the home of iridescent chitchat.

He said he would a small cabin build there, of clay and wattles made.

Everybody said did he mean he would build a small cabin there, made of clay and wattles?

Mr. Lionel Fortague said yes, but his way of putting it was more poetic.

Everybody said maybe, but they were all out of wattles.

Mr. Lionel Fortague grew very angry at the people of
Innisfree.

He a small cabin built there, of clay and beaverboard made.

He a fierce-looking dog at an annual clearance sale bought,
and it the people of Innisfree one by one to bite he
instructed.

My, he was disappointed.

He had forgotten that a bargain dog never bites.

### THE PURIST

I give you now Professor Twist,
A conscientious scientist.
Trustees exclaimed, "He never bungles!"
And sent him off to distant jungles.
Camped on a tropic riverside,

One day he missed his loving bride.
She had, the guide informed him later,
Been eaten by an alligator.
Professor Twist could not but smile.
"You mean," he said, "a crocodile."

## THE KITTEN

The trouble with a kitten is
THAT
Eventually it becomes a
CAT.

## THE LION

Oh, weep for Mr. and Mrs. Bryan!
He was eaten by a lion;
Following which, the lion's lioness
Up and swallowed Bryan's Bryaness.

## THE FLY

The Lord in His wisdom made the fly
And then forgot to tell us why.

## THE TERMITE

Some primal termite knocked on wood
And tasted it, and found it good,
And that is why your Cousin May
Fell through the parlor floor today.

## THE TURKEY

There is nothing more perky
Than a masculine turkey.
When he struts he struts
With no ifs or buts.
When his face is apoplectic
His harem grows hectic,
And when he gobbles
Their universe wobbles.

## SHRINKING SONG

Woollen socks, woollen socks!
Full of color, full of clocks!
Plain and fancy, yellow, blue,
From the counter beam at you.
O golden fleece, O magic flocks!
O irresistible woollen socks!
O happy haberdasher's clerk
Amid that galaxy to work!
And now it festers, now it rankles
Not to have them round your ankles;
Now with your conscience do you spar;
They look expensive, and they are;
Now conscience whispers, You ought not to,
And human nature roars, You've got to!
Woollen socks, woollen socks!
First you buy them in a box.
You buy them several sizes large,
Fit for Hercules, or a barge.

You buy them thus because you think
These lovely woollen socks may shrink.
At home you don your socks with ease,
You find the heels contain your knees;
You realize with saddened heart
Their toes and yours are far apart.
You take them off and mutter Bosh,
You up and send them to the wash.
Too soon, too soon the socks return,
Too soon the horrid truth you learn;
Your woollen socks can not be worn
Unless a midget child is born,
And either sockless you must go,
Or buy a sock for every toe.
Woollen socks, woollen socks!
Infuriating paradox!
Hosiery wonderful and terrible,
Heaven to wear, and yet unwearable.
The man enmeshed in such a quandary
Can only hie him to the laundry,
And while his socks are hung to dry,
Wear them once as they're shrinking by.


## YOU AND ME AND P. B. SHELLEY

What is life? Life is stepping down a step or sitting in a
     chair,
And it isn't there.
Life is not having been told that the man has just waxed
     the floor,
It is pulling doors marked PUSH and pushing doors marked

PULL and not noticing notices which say PLEASE USE
OTHER DOOR.
It is when you diagnose a sore throat as an unprepared
geography lesson and send your child weeping to
school only to be returned an hour later covered with
spots that are indubitably genuine,
It is a concert with a trombone soloist filling in for Yehudi
Menuhin.
Were it not for frustration and humiliation
I suppose the human race would get ideas above its sta-
tion.
Somebody once described Shelley as a beautiful and inef-
fective angel beating his luminous wings against the
void in vain,
Which is certainly describing with might and main,
But probably means that we are all brothers under our pelts,
And Shelley went around pulling doors marked PUSH and
pushing doors marked PULL just like everybody else.

## THE FIREFLY

The firefly's flame
Is something for which science has no name.
I can think of nothing eerier
Than flying around with an unidentified glow on a person's
posteerier.

## THE SHARK

How many scientists have written
The shark is gentle as a kitten!
Yet this I know about the shark:
His bite is worser than his bark.

[   43   ]

## THE WASP

The wasp and all his numerous family
I look upon as a major calamily.
He throws open his nest with prodigality,
But I distrust his waspitality.

## BARMAIDS ARE DIVINER THAN MERMAIDS

Fish are very good at swimming,
And the ocean with them is brimming.
They stay under water all year round,
And they never get drowned,
And they have a gift more precious than gold,
Which is that they never get cold.

No, they may not be as tasty as venison or mooseflesh,
But they never get gooseflesh.
They have been in the ocean since they were roe,
So they don't have to creep into it toe by toe,
And also they stay in it permanently, which must be a
    source of great satisfaction,
Because they don't have to run dripping and shivering up
    and down the beach waiting vainly for a healthy
    reaction.
Indeed when I think how uncomplicated the ocean is for
    fish my thoughts grow jealous and scathing,
Because when fish bump into another fish it doesn't wring
    from them a cry of Faugh! and ruin their day's bathing.
No, if it's a bigger fish than they are, they turn around
    and beat it,
And if it's littler, they eat it.
Some fish are striped and some are speckled,
But none of them ever heard of ultra-violet rays and felt
    it necessary to lie around getting sand in their eyes
    and freckled.
Oh, would it not be wondrous to be a fish? No, it would
    not be wondrous,
Because we unmarine humans are at the top of the animal
    kingdom and it would be very undignified to change
    places with anything under us.

### SPRING SONG

Listen, buds, it's March twenty-first;
Don't you know enough to burst?
Come on, birds, unlock your throats!

Come on, gardeners, shed your coats!
Come on zephyrs, come on flowers,
Come on grass, and violet showers!
And come on, lambs, in frisking flocks!
Salute the vernal equinox!
Twang the cheerful lute and zither!
Spring is absolutely hither!
Yester eve was dark despair,
With winter, winter, everywhere;
Today, upon the other hand,
'Tis spring throughout this happy land.
Oh, such is Nature's chiaroscuro,
According to the Weather Bureau.

Then giddy-ap, Napoleon! Giddy-ap, Gideon!
The sun has crossed the right meridian!
What though the blasts of Winter sting?
Officially, at least, it's Spring,
And be it far from our desire
To make the Weather Man a liar!

So, blossom, ye parks, with cozy benches,
Occupied by blushing wenches!
Pipe, ye frogs, while swains are sighing,
And furnaces unwept are dying!
Crow, ye cocks, a little bit louder!
Mount, ye sales of paint and powder!
Croon, ye crooner, yet more croonishly!
Shine, ye moon, a lot more moonishly!
And oh ye brooklets, burst your channels!
And oh ye camphor, greet ye flannels!
And bloom, ye clothesline, bloom with wash,

Where erstwhile squudged the grim galosh!
Ye transit lines, abet our follies
By turning loose your open trolleys!
And ye, ye waking hibernators,
Drain anti-freeze from your radiators!
While ye, ye otherwise useless dove,
Remember, please, to rhyme with love.

Then giddy-ap, Napoleon! Giddy-ap, Gideon!
The sun has crossed the right meridian!
What though the blasts of Winter sting?
Officially, at least, it's Spring!

## THE GANDER

Be careful not to cross the gander,
A bird composed of beak and dander.
His heart is filled with prideful hate
Of all the world except his mate,
And if the neighbors do not err
He's overfond of beating her.
Is she happy? What's the use
Of trying to psychoanalyze a goose?

## THE GRACKLE

The grackle's voice is less than mellow,
His heart is black, his eye is yellow,
He bullies more attractive birds
With hoodlum deeds and vulgar words,
And should a human interfere,
Attacks that human in the rear.
I cannot help but deem the grackle
An ornithological debacle.

## THE PORPOISE

I kind of like the playful porpoise,
A healthy mind in a healthy corpus.
He and his cousin, the playful dolphin,
Why they like swimmin like I like golphin.

## TIME MARCHES ON

You ask me, brothers, why I flinch.
Well, I will tell you, inch by inch.
Is it not proper cause for fright
That what is day will soon be night?
Evenings I flinch the selfsame way,
For what is night will soon be day.
At five o'clock it chills my gore
Simply to know it isn't four.
How Sunday into Monday melts!
And every month is something else.
If Summer on the ladder lingers,
Autumn tramples upon her fingers,
Fleeing before the jostling train
Of Winter, and Spring, and Summer again.
Year swallows year and licks its lips,
Then down the gullet of next year slips.
We chip at Time with clocks and watches;
We flee him in love and double scotches;
Even as we scatter in alarm
He marches with us, arm in arm;
Though while we sleep, he forward rides,
Yet when we wake, he's at our sides.
While grandly paying no attention to us

He's doing things I hate to mention to us.
His the chain letter never broken;
For each, each day he leaves some token;
Let men walk straight or let them err,
He never leaves them as they were.
While ladies draw their stockings on
The ladies they were are up and gone.
I pen my lines, I finish, I scan them,
I'm not the poet who began them.
Each moment Time, the lord of changers,
Stuffs our skins with ephemeral strangers.
Good heavens, how remote from me
The billion people I used to be!
Flinch with me, brothers, why not flinch,
Shirts caught in the eternal winch?
Come, let us flinch till Time stands still;
Although I do not think he will.
Hark brothers, to the dismal proof:
The seconds spattering on the roof!

### THE EEL

I don't mind eels
Except as meals.
And the way they feels.

### GOOD–BY, BUGS

Some insects feed on rosebuds,
And others feed on carrion.
Between them they devour the earth.
Bugs are totalitarian.

[ 49 ]

## THE GERM

A mighty creature is the germ,
Though smaller than the pachyderm.
His customary dwelling place
Is deep within the human race.
His childish pride he often pleases
By giving people strange diseases.
Do you, my poppet, feel infirm?
You probably contain a germ.

## THE RHINOCEROS

The rhino is a homely beast,
For human eyes he's not a feast.
Farewell, farewell, you old rhinoceros,
I'll stare at something less prepoceros.

## A WORD ON WIND

Cows go around saying Moo,
But the wind goes around saying Woooo.
Ghosts say Woooo to you, too,
And sometimes they say Boo to you, too,
But everybody has heard the wind and few people have
     heard a ghost,
So it is commonly supposed that the wind says Woooo the
     most.
Scientists try to tell us that wind is caused by atmospheric
     conditions at the North Pole or over distant Canadian
     ranches,

But I guess scientists don't ever get to the country because everybody who has ever been in the country knows that wind is caused by the trees waggling their branches.

On the ocean, where there are no trees, they refer to the wind as gales,

And it is probably caused by whales,

And in the Sahara, where there are no trees or whales either, they call the wind a simoom or something,

And it is the result of the profanation of Tutankhamen's tomb or something,

But anyhow wherever you are, the wind is always nigh and I for one hope it won't come any nigher,

Because it makes cold colder and heat hotter and rain wetter and dust drier,

And it can cover a lot of time in a very short space,

And it doesn't matter whether it's an East Wind and you are heading West or a North Wind and you are heading South, it always manages to be right in your face.

Ill winds blow nobody good and they also blow new hats into mud puddles and voracious clouds of mosquitoes into propinquity with your hide,

And they make your cigarette burn down on just one side.

Some people are very refined,

And when they recite poetry or sing songs they pronounce wind, wined.

Well, dear wined, every time you say Wooooo,

Why I wish you would say it to people who say wined, right after you have said it somewhere where somebody is making fertilizer or glue.

## SONG BEFORE BREAKFAST

Hopeful each morning I arise
And splash the cobwebs from my eyes.
I brush my teeth and scrape my chin
And bravely at the mirror grin.
Sternly I force myself to say,
Huzza! huzza! another day!
Oh happy me! oh lucky I!
Another chance with life to vie!
Another golden opportunity
To rise and shine in this community!
Another target for my aim!
Another whack at wealth and fame!
Almost I feel within me stir
A budding force of character.
Who knows, indeed, but what I might
Perhaps have altered overnight?
Today may be the day, who knows,
That sees me triumph o'er my foes:
Gluttony, simony, and sloth,
And drawing on the table cloth;
Perjury, arson, envy, pride,
And renting tales of homicide;
Barratry, avarice and wrath
And blowing bubbles in the bath.
The differences this day may bring!
Perhaps I'll work like anything;
I'll travel to my tasks on foot,
And in the bank the carfare put,
And buy a haircut when I need it,
And if I get a letter, read it,

And every eve improve myself
With Shakespeare or the Five Foot Shelf.
The things I want to do, I won't,
And only do the things I don't.
What lordly aspirations dawn
The while I draw my trousers on!
Oh beamish morning, big with hope
And noble tasks with which to cope,
If I should fail you, do not sorrow;
I'll be a better man tomorrow.


## THE PIG

The pig, if I am not mistaken,
Supplies us sausage, ham, and bacon.
Let others say his heart is big —
I call it stupid of the pig.


## THE POULTRIES

Let's think of eggs.
They have no legs.
Chickens come from eggs
But they have legs.
The plot thickens;
Eggs come from chickens,
But have no legs under 'em.
What a conundrum!

# THE LAMB

Little gamboling lamb,
Do you know where you am?
In a patch of mint.
I'll give you a hint.
Scram,
Lamb!

## THE OCTOPUS

Tell me, O Octopus, I begs,
Is those things arms, or is they legs?
I marvel at thee, Octopus;
If I were thou, I'd call me Us.

## THE CAMEL

The camel has a single hump;
The dromedary, two;
Or else the other way around.
I'm never sure. Are you?

Isabel met an enormous bear,
Isabel, Isabel, didn't care;
The bear was hungry, the bear was ravenous,
The bear's big mouth was cruel and cavernous.
The bear said, Isabel, glad to meet you,
How do, Isabel, now I'll eat you!
Isabel, Isabel, didn't worry,
Isabel didn't scream or scurry.
She washed her hands and she straightened her hair up,
Then Isabel quietly ate the bear up.

Once in a night as black as pitch
Isabel met a wicked old witch.
The witch's face was cross and wrinkled,
The witch's gums with teeth were sprinkled.
Ho ho, Isabel! the old witch crowed,
I'll turn you into an ugly toad!
Isabel, Isabel, didn't worry,
Isabel didn't scream or scurry,
She showed no rage and she showed no rancor,
But she turned the witch into milk and drank her.

Isabel met a hideous giant,
Isabel continued self-reliant.
The giant was hairy, the giant was horrid,
He had one eye in the middle of his forehead.
Good morning Isabel, the giant said,
I'll grind your bones to make my bread.
Isabel, Isabel, didn't worry,
Isabel didn't scream or scurry.

She nibbled the zwieback that she always fed off,
And when it was gone, she cut the giant's head off.

Isabel met a troublesome doctor,
He punched and he poked till he really shocked her.
The doctor's talk was of coughs and chills
And the doctor's satchel bulged with pills.
The doctor said unto Isabel,
Swallow this, it will make you well.
Isabel, Isabel, didn't worry,
Isabel didn't scream or scurry.
She took those pills from the pill concocter,
And Isabel calmly cured the doctor.

## CREEPS AND CRAWLS

The insect world appealed to Fabre.
I find the insect world macabre.
In every hill of ants I see
A governed glimpse of what shall be,
And sense in every web contriver
Man's predecessor and survivor.
Someday, perhaps, my citronella
Will rank with Chamberlain's umbrella.

## THE ABSENTEES

I'd ride a cock horse to Banbury Cross
For giblet gravy and cranberry sauce,
Two treats which are held in reserve by the waiter
Till you've finished your turkey and mashed potater.

# THE BIG TENT UNDER THE ROOF

Noises new to sea and land
Issue from the circus band.
Each musician looks like mumps
From blowing umpah umpah umps.

Lovely girls in spangled pants
Ride on gilded elephants.
Elephants are useful friends,
They have handles on both ends;
They hold each other's hindmost handles
And flee from mice and Roman candles.
Their hearts are gold, their hides are emery,
And they have a most tenacious memory.

Notice also, girls and boys,
The circus horses' avoirdupois.
Far and wide the wily scouts
Seek these snow-white stylish stouts.
Calmer steeds were never found
Unattached to a merry-go-round.
Equestriennes prefer to jump
Onto horses pillow-plump.

Equestriennes will never ride
As other people do, astride.
They like to balance on one foot,
And wherever they get, they won't stay put.
They utter frequent whoops and yips,
And have the most amazing hips.
Pink seems to be their favorite color,
And very few things are very much duller.

Yet I for one am more than willing
That everything should be less thrilling.
My heart and lungs both bound and balk
When high-wire walkers start to walk.
They ought to perish, yet they don't;
Some fear they will, some fear they won't.

I lack the adjectives, verbs and nouns
To do full justice to the clowns.
Their hearts are constantly breaking, I hear,
And who am I to interfere?
I'd rather shake hands with Mr. Ringling
And tell him his circus is a beautiful thingling.

### LATHER AS YOU GO

Beneath this slab
John Brown is stowed.
He watched the ads,
And not the road.

## IT IS INDEED SPINACH

People by whom I am riled

Are people who go around wishing O that Time would backward turn backward and again make them a child.

Either they have no sense, or else they go around repeating something they have heard, like a parakeet,

Or else they deliberately prevarikete,

Because into being a marathon dancer or a chiropodist or a tea-taster or a certified public accountant I could not be beguiled,

But I could sooner than I could into being again a child,

Because being a child is not much of a pastime,

And I don't want any next time because I remember the last time.

I do not wish to play with my toes,

Nor do I wish to have codliver oil spooned down my throat
or albolene pushed up my nose.
I don't want to be plopped at sundown into a crib or a
cradle
And if I don't go to sleep right away be greeted with either
a lullaby or an upbraidal.
I can think of nothing worse
Than never being out of sight of a parent or nurse:
Yes, that is the part that I don't see how they survive it,
To have their private life so far from private.
Furthermore, I don't want to cry for the moon,
And I do want to hold my own spoon;
I have more ambitious ideas of a lark
Than to collect pebbles in my hat or be taken for a walk
in the park;
I should hate to be held together with safety pins instead
of buttons and suspenders and belts,
And I should particularly hate being told every time I
was doing something I liked that it was time to do
something else.
So it's pooh for the people who want Time to make them
a child again because I think they must already be a
child again or else they would stand up and own up
That it's much more fun to be a grown-up.


### REQUIEM

There was a young belle of old Natchez
Whose garments were always in patchez.
When comment arose
On the state of her clothes,
She drawled, When Ah itchez, Ah scratchez!

## SONG FOR DITHERERS

I journey not whence nor whither,
I languish alone in a dither;
I journey not to nor fro,
And my dither to me I owe.
I could find a pleasanter name for it
Had I somebody else to blame for it,
But alas that beneath the sun
Dithers are built for one.
This is the song of the dither,
For viol, bassoon or zither,
Till the greenest simpletons wither
This is the song of the dither;
When regular troubles are wrong with you,
Others are guilty along with you;
Dithers are private trouble
Where you privately stew and bubble.
Come hither, somebody, come hither,
Would you care for a share of my dither?
I want somebody else to be mad at;
"Have at you!" to cry, and be had at.
I am tired of being angry at me,
There is room in my dither for three,
There is room in my dither for two;
We could butt at each other and moo;
We could hiss like the serpent, and slither
Through the tropical depths of my dither;
Like bees we could fight along beelines,
Or spit at each other like felines;
I care not who gaineth the laurel,
All I want is a foe and a quarrel.

Alone in my dither I pine.
For the sake of the days of lang syne,
For your white-haired old feyther and mither,
Come along, come along to my dither.
With no foe in my dither but me,
I swoon, I lay doon, and I dee.


## THE TALE OF CUSTARD THE DRAGON

Belinda lived in a little white house,
With a little black kitten and a little gray mouse,
And a little yellow dog and a little red wagon,
And a realio, trulio, little pet dragon.

Now the name of the little black kitten was Ink,
And the little gray mouse, she called her Blink,
And the little yellow dog was sharp as Mustard,
But the dragon was a coward, and she called him Custard.

Custard the dragon had big sharp teeth,
And spikes on top of him and scales underneath,
Mouth like a fireplace, chimney for a nose,
And realio, trulio daggers on his toes.

Belinda was as brave as a barrel full of bears,
And Ink and Blink chased lions down the stairs,
Mustard was as brave as a tiger in a rage,
But Custard cried for a nice safe cage.

Belinda tickled him, she tickled him unmerciful,
Ink, Blink and Mustard, they rudely called him Percival,

They all sat laughing in the little red wagon
At the realio, trulio, cowardly dragon.

Belinda giggled till she shook the house,
And Blink said Weeck! which is giggling for a mouse,
Ink and Mustard rudely asked his age,
When Custard cried for a nice safe cage.

Suddenly, suddenly they heard a nasty sound,
And Mustard growled, and they all looked around.
Meowch! cried Ink, and Ooh! cried Belinda,
For there was a pirate, climbing in the winda.

Pistol in his left hand, pistol in his right,
And he held in his teeth a cutlass bright,
His beard was black, one leg was wood;
It was clear that the pirate meant no good.

Belinda paled, and she cried Help! Help!
But Mustard fled with a terrified yelp,
Ink trickled down to the bottom of the household,
And little mouse Blink strategically mouseholed.

But up jumped Custard, snorting like an engine,
Clashed his tail like irons in a dungeon,
With a clatter and a clank and a jangling squirm
He went at the pirate like a robin at a worm.

The pirate gaped at Belinda's dragon,
And gulped some grog from his pocket flagon,

He fired two bullets, but they didn't hit,
And Custard gobbled him, every bit.

Belinda embraced him, Mustard licked him,
No one mourned for his pirate victim.
Ink and Blink in glee did gyrate
Around the dragon that ate the pyrate.

Belinda still lives in her little white house,
With her little black kitten and her little gray mouse,
And her little yellow dog and her little red wagon,
And her realio, trulio, little pet dragon.

Belinda is as brave as a barrel full of bears,
And Ink and Blink chase lions down the stairs.
Mustard is as brave as a tiger in a rage,
But Custard keeps crying for a nice safe cage.

## TO A SMALL BOY STANDING ON MY SHOES WHILE I AM WEARING THEM

Let's straighten this out, my little man,
And reach an agreement if we can.
I entered your door as an honored guest.
My shoes are shined and my trousers are pressed,
And I won't stretch out and read you the funnies
And I won't pretend that we're Easter bunnies.
If you must get somebody down on the floor,
What do you think your parents are for?
I do not like the things that you say
And I hate the games that you want to play.

No matter how frightfully hard you try,
We've little in common, you and I.
The interest I take in my neighbor's nursery
Would have to grow, to be even cursory,
And I would that performing sons and nephews
Were carted away with the daily refuse,
And I hold that frolicsome daughters and nieces
Are ample excuse for breaking leases.
You may take a sock at your daddy's tummy,
Or climb all over your doting mummy,
But keep your attentions to me in check,
Or, sonny boy, I will wring your neck.
A happier man today I'd be
Had someone wrung it ahead of me.

## NOT EVEN FOR BRUNCH

When branches bend in fruitful stupor
Before the woods break out in plaid,
The super-market talks more super,
The roadside stands go slightly mad.
What garden grew this goblin harvest?
Who coined these words that strike me numb?
I will not purchase, though I starvest,
The cuke, the glad, the lope, the mum.

In happier days I sank to slumber
Murmuring names as sweet as hope:
Fair gladiolus, and cucumber,
Chrysanthemum and cantaloupe.
I greet the changelings that awoke me

[ 65 ]

With warmth a little less than luke,
As farmer and florist crowd to choke me
With glad and lope, with mum and cuke.

Go hence, far hence, you jargon-mongers,
Go soak your head in boiling ads,
Go feed to cuttlefish and congers
Your mums and lopes, your cukes and glads.
Stew in the whimsy that you dole us;
I roam where magic casements ope
On cantemum spiced, and cuciolus,
On chrysanthecumber, and gladaloupe.

## THE BOY WHO LAUGHED AT SANTA CLAUS

In Baltimore there lived a boy.
He wasn't anybody's joy.
Although his name was Jabez Dawes,

His character was full of flaws.
In school he never led his classes,
He hid old ladies' reading glasses,
His mouth was open when he chewed,
And elbows to the table glued.
He stole the milk of hungry kittens,
And walked through doors marked No ADMITTANCE.
He said he acted thus because
There wasn't any Santa Claus.
Another trick that tickled Jabez
Was crying "Boo!" at little babies.
He brushed his teeth, they said in town,
Sideways instead of up and down.

Yet people pardoned every sin,
And viewed his antics with a grin,
Till they were told by Jabez Dawes,
"There isn't any Santa Claus!"
Deploring how he did behave,
His parents swiftly sought their grave.
They hurried through the portals pearly,
And Jabez left the funeral early.

Like whooping cough, from child to child,
He sped to spread the rumor wild:
"Sure as my name is Jabez Dawes
There isn't any Santa Claus!"
Slunk like a weasel or a marten
Through nursery and kindergarten,
Whispering low to every tot,
"There isn't any, no there's not!"

The children wept all Christmas Eve
And Jabez chortled up his sleeve.
No infant dared hang up his stocking
For fear of Jabez' ribald mocking.
He sprawled on his untidy bed,
Fresh malice dancing in his head,
When presently with scalp a-tingling,
Jabez heard a distant jingling;
He heard the crunch of sleigh and hoof
Crisply alighting on the roof.

What good to rise and bar the door?
A shower of soot was on the floor.
What was beheld by Jabez Dawes?
The fireplace full of Santa Claus!
Then Jabez fell upon his knees
With cries of "Don't," and "Pretty please."
He howled, "I don't know where you read it,
But anyhow, I never said it!"

"Jabez," replied the angry saint,
"It isn't I, it's you that ain't.
Although there is a Santa Claus,
There isn't any Jabez Dawes!"
Said Jabez then with impudent vim,
"Oh, yes there is; and I am him!
Your magic don't scare me, it doesn't" —
And suddenly he found he wasn't!

From grimy feet to grimy locks,
Jabez became a Jack-in-the-box,
An ugly toy with springs unsprung,

Forever sticking out his tongue.
The neighbors heard his mournful squeal;
They searched for him, but not with zeal.
No trace was found of Jabez Dawes,
Which led to thunderous applause,
And people drank a loving cup
And went and hung their stockings up.

All you who sneer at Santa Claus,
Beware the fate of Jabez Dawes,
The saucy boy who mocked the saint.
Donder and Blitzen licked off his paint.


## A WATCHED EXAMPLE NEVER BOILS

The weather is so very mild
That some would call it warm.
Good gracious, aren't we lucky, child?
Here comes a thunderstorm.

The sky is now indelible ink,
The garden is a raging sea,
But you and I, we do not shrink;
We love the lovely thunder.

The garden is a raging sea,
The hurricane is snarling;
Oh happy you and happy me!
Isn't the lightning darling?

Fear not the thunder, little one.
It's weather, simply weather;

It's friendly giants full of fun
Clapping their hands together.

I hope of lightning our supply
Will never be exhausted;
You know it's lanterns in the sky
For angels who are losted.

We watch in glee the fairy trail
The jolly thunderbolt,
We watch in glee the fairy trail
Of ampere, watt, and volt.

Oh, than to enjoy a storm like this
There's nothing I would rather.
Don't dive beneath the blankets, Miss!
Or else leave room for Father.

## PEDIATRIC REFLECTION

Many an infant screams like a calliope
Could be soothed by a little attention to its diope.

## CHILDREN'S PARTY

May I join you in the doghouse, Rover?
I wish to retire till the party's over.
Since three o'clock I've done my best
To entertain each tiny guest;
My conscience now I've left behind me,

And if they want me, let them find me.
I blew their bubbles, I sailed their boats,
I kept them from each other's throats.
I told them tales of magic lands,
I took them out to wash their hands.
I sorted their rubbers and tied their laces,
I wiped their noses and dried their faces.
Of similarity there's lots
'Twixt tiny tots and Hottentots.
I've earned repose to heal the ravages
Of these angelic-looking savages.
Oh, progeny playing by itself
Is a lonely fascinating elf,
But progeny in roistering batches
Would drive St. Francis from here to Natchez.
Shunned are the games a parent proposes;
They prefer to squirt each other with hoses,
Their playmates are their natural foemen
And they like to poke each other's abdomen.
Their joy needs another's woe to cushion it
Say a puddle, and somebody littler to push in it.
They observe with glee the ballistic results
Of ice cream with spoons for catapults,
And inform the assembly with tears and glares
That everyone's presents are better than theirs.
Oh, little women and little men,
Someday I hope to love you again,
But not till after the party's over,
So give me the key to the doghouse, Rover.

When I was but a boy,
'Twas my once-a-yearly joy
To arise of a Yuletide morning,
And eagerly behold
The crimson and the gold
Of the messages the mantelpiece adorning.
There were angels, there were squires,
There were steeples, there were spires,
There were villagers, and mistletoe and holly,
There were cosy English inns
With the snow around their chins,
And I innocently thought them rather jolly.
I blush for me, but by your leave,
I'm afraid that I am still naïve.

Oh, give me an old-fashioned Christmas card,
With mistletoe galore, and holly by the yard,
With galumptious greens and gorgeous scarlets,
With crackling logs and apple-cheeked varlets,
With horses prancing down a frosty road,
And a stagecoach laden with a festive load,
And the light from the wayside windows streaming,
And a white moon rising and one star gleaming.

Departed is the time
Of Christmases sublime;
My soprano is now a mezzo-basso;
And the mantelpiece contains
The angular remains
Of a later representative Picasso.

There are circles, there are dots,
There are corners, there are spots,
There are modernistic snapshots of the city;
Or, when the artist lags,
They are livened up with gags.
You must choose between the arty and the witty.
I blush for me, but I must say
I wish you'd take them all away.

Oh, give me an old-fashioned Christmas card,
With hostlers hostling in an old inn yard,
With church bells chiming their silver notes,
And jolly red squires in their jolly red coats,
And a good fat goose by the fire that dangles,
And a few more angels and a few less angles.
Turn backward, Time, to please this bard,
And give me an old-fashioned Christmas card.


### AFTER THE CHRISTENING

Come along, everybody, see the pretty baby,
Such a pretty baby ought to be adored.
Come along, everybody, come and bore the baby,
See the pretty baby, begging to be bored.

Hurry, hurry, Aunt Louise,
Silly names are sure to please.
Bother what the baby thinks!
Call her Kitchy-kitch and Binks,
Call her Wackywoo and Snookums,
Just ignore her dirty lookums,

Who then she is fairer game
For every kind of silly name?
Baby cannot answer back,
Or perhaps an aunt she'd lack.

Come along, everybody, isn't she a darling?
Such a little darling ought to be enjoyed.
Come along, everybody, let's annoy the baby,
Such a darling darling begs to be annoyed.

Goodness Gracious, Uncle George!
Home at last from Valley Forge?
Won't you try on her the whoops
That cheered the Continental troops?
Stand a little closer, please;
That will put her at her ease;
And babies find it hard to hear,
So place your mouth against her ear —
I guess she heard it, Uncle George;
I'm sure they did at Valley Forge.

Come along, everybody, see the little lady,
Isn't she adorable and kissable and pleasing?
Come along, everybody, come and tease the baby,
Here's a lady baby available for teasing!

Cousin Charles was always chummy;
He's about to poke her tummy.
Grandpa almost chokes on chuckles,
Tickling with his beard her knuckles;
All of Granny's muscles ache
From half an hour of patty-cake;

God-mamma with glee begins
A noisy count of baby's chins;
God-papa with humor glows
Playing piggie with her toes.
See the happy prideful parents,
Do they think of interference?
Certainly not, while baby gives
Such wholesome fun to relatives.

Up and at her, everybody, at the pretty baby,
Tell her she's a dumpling, tell her she's a dear.
Everybody knows the way to woo a baby —
Tickle her and pinch her and yodel in her ear.


### GENEALOGICAL REFLECTION

No McTavish
Was ever lavish.


### MORE ABOUT PEOPLE

When people aren't asking questions
They're making suggestions
And when they're not doing one of those
They're either looking over your shoulder or stepping on
    your toes
And then as if that weren't enough to annoy you
They employ you.
Anybody at leisure
Incurs everybody's displeasure.
It seems to be very irking

To people at work to see other people not working,
So they tell you that work is wonderful medicine,
Just look at Firestone and Ford and Edison,
And they lecture you till they're out of breath or something
And then if you don't succumb they starve you to death
    or something.
All of which results in a nasty quirk:
That if you don't want to work you have to work to earn
    enough money so that you won't have to work.


## GOODY FOR OUR SIDE AND YOUR SIDE TOO

Foreigners are people somewhere else,
Natives are people at home;
If the place you're at is your habitat,
You're a foreigner, say in Rome.
But the scales of Justice balance true,
And tit only leads to tat,
So the man who's at home when he stays in Rome
Is abroad when he's where you're at.

When we leave the limits of the land in which
Our birth certificates sat us,
It does not mean just a change of scene,
But also a change of status.
The Frenchman with his fetching beard,
The Scot with his kilt and sporran,
One moment he may a native be,
And the next may find him foreign.

[ 76 ]

There's many a difference quickly found
Between the different races,
But the only essential differential
Is living in different places.
Yet such is the pride of prideful man,
From Austrians to Australians,
That wherever he is, he regards as his,
And the natives there, as aliens.

Oh, I'll be friends if you'll be friends,
The foreigner tells the native,
And we'll work together for our common ends
Like a preposition and a dative.
If our common ends seem mostly mine,
Why not, you ignorant foreigner?
And the native replies contrariwise;
And hence, my dears, the coroner.

So mind your manners when a native, please,
And doubly when you're not,
And Vickers and Krupp will soon fold up,
And Sopwith pawn his yacht.
One simple thought, if you have it pat,
Will eliminate the coroner:
You may be a native in your habitat,
But to foreigners you're just a foreigner.

## I'LL TAKE THE HIGH ROAD COMMISSION

In between the route marks
And the shaving rhymes,

Black and yellow markers
Comment on the times.

All along the highway
Hear the signs discourse:

MEN
SLOW
WORKING

;

SADDLE
CROSSING
HORSE

.

Cryptic crossroad preachers
Proffer good advice,
Helping wary drivers
Keep out of Paradise.

Transcontinental sermons,
Transcendental talk:

SOFT
CAUTION
SHOULDERS

;

CROSS
CHILDREN
WALK

.

Wisest of their proverbs,
Truest of their talk,
Have I found that dictum:

[ 78 ]

CROSS
# CHILDREN
WALK

.

When Adam took the highway
He left his sons a guide:

CROSS
# CHILDREN
WALK

;

CHEERFUL
# CHILDREN
RIDE

.


## SONG OF THE OPEN ROAD

I think that I shall never see
A billboard lovely as a tree.
Indeed, unless the billboards fall
I'll never see a tree at all.


## MR. PEACHEY'S PREDICAMENT
### or
## NO MOT PARADES

Once there was a man named Mr. Peachey and he lived
on Park Avenue and played the harp and was an
eligible bachelor but his social life was hapless,

And he thought at first it was because his parents came from
    Indianapless,
But one day he awoke from a troubled nap,
And said I am tired of this hapless social life, what I want
    is a social life simply teeming with hap.
It can't be, he said, that I don't play the harp enough,
I wonder if just possibly my wits are not sharp enough.
I know that I'm pretty noted
But I've never been quoted;
Perhaps the solution for me
Is some effervescent repartee;
Suppose before I next dine out I compose a series of
    epigrams of searing astringency
And then I shall be ready with a quip for any conversational
    contingency.
So he composed a series of epigrams of indubitable variety,
And went to dine with some people way up in society.
And in the taxi he memorized his lines and held a solo
    rehearsal,
And he was delighted, because he said some people's humor
    is specialized but mine is universal.
There may well be a Mr. Shoemaker there who has divorced
    a beautiful rich virtuous wife for a debt-ridden hideous
    wife with a past,
And I'll say Shoemaker you should have stuck to your last;
And suppose somebody remarks that the hostess looks like
    a Titian I bring them up short,
I can answer, Looks like a Titian, eh? Do you mean beaut-
    or mort-?
And I'll go right on and say While we're on the subject
    of waltzes I'd like to play a little Haydn for you, and
    I'll go to the piano and grope at the keys and then
    look up impishly and speak,

And say I really don't know whether I'm playing Haydn
   or Haydn seek.
Then after the laughter has died down I shall approach
   some Yale man who has just returned from abroad
   whom I wish to embarrass
And I'll ask him how he enjoyed the Boola-Boolavards of
   Paris.
Oh, said Mr. Peachey gleefully, the days of my hapless
   social life are over, I cannot help but be a wow,
I wish I was at the party right now.
But when he got to the party his hostess, who didn't look
   like a Titian at all, she looked like a Dali, was quite
   sharp,
And sent him right back to his Park Avenue apartment
   to get his harp,
And today he is living in the old family mansion in
   Indianapless
Where I'm sorry to say his social life is just as hapless.


### EPISTLE TO THE OLYMPIANS

Dear parents, I write you this letter
Because I thought I'd better;
Because I would like to know
Exactly which way to grow.

My milk I will leave undrunk
If you'd rather have me shrunk,
If your love it will further kindle,
I'll do my best to dwindle;

Or, on the other hand,
Do you wish me to expand?

I'll stuff like a greedy rajah
If you really want me larger.

All that I ask of you
Is to tell me which to do;
To whisper in accents mild
The proper size for a child.

I get so very confused
By the chidings commonly used.
Am I really such a dunce
As to err two ways at once?

When one mood you are in,
My bigness is a sin:
"Oh what a thing to do
For a great big girl like you!"

But then another time
Smallness is my crime:
"Stop doing whatever you're at;
You're far too little for that!"

Kind parents, be so kind
As to kindly make up your mind
And whisper in accents mild
The proper size for a child.


## PRETTY HALCYON DAYS

How pleasant to sit on the beach,
On the beach, on the sand, in the sun,

With ocean galore within reach,
And nothing at all to be done!
No letters to answer,
No bills to be burned,
No work to be shirked,
No cash to be earned.
It is pleasant to sit on the beach
With nothing at all to be done.

How pleasant to look at the ocean,
Democratic and damp; indiscriminate;
It fills me with noble emotion
To think I am able to swim in it.
To lave in the wave,
Majestic and chilly,
Tomorrow I crave;
But today it is silly.
It is pleasant to look at the ocean;
Tomorrow, perhaps, I shall swim in it.

How pleasant to gaze at the sailors,
As their sailboats they manfully sail
With the vigor of vikings and whalers
In the days of the viking and whale.
They sport on the brink
Of the shad and the shark;
If it's windy they sink;
If it isn't, they park.
It is pleasant to gaze at the sailors,
To gaze without having to sail.

How pleasant the salt anaesthetic
Of the air and the sand and the sun;

Leave the earth to the strong and athletic,
And the sea to adventure upon.
But the sun and the sand
No contractor can copy;
We lie in the land
Of the lotus and poppy;
We vegetate, calm and aesthetic,
On the beach, on the sand, in the sun.


## ARTHUR

There was an old man of Calcutta,
Who coated his tonsils with butta,
Thus converting his snore
From a thunderous roar
To a soft, oleaginous mutta.

## THE INDIVIDUALIST

Once there was a man named Jarvis Gravel who was just
    a man named Jarvis Gravel except for one thing:
He hated spring.
And this was because once a Communist had said Come
    on down to Union Square, it's May Day,
And Jarvis went, thinking he had said Come on down to
    Union Square, it's pay day.
So from then on anything at all vernal
Was to him strictly infernal.
When he saw the first crocus poke its head up

He'd get a shovel and dig the entire bed up,
And he bought a horse and galloped back and forth
Tipping off the worms when the first robin started North.
To love the way of a man with a maid in the moonlight
    was something he never learnt,
And he spent a lot of beautiful balmy evenings moving
    FRESH PAINT signs from park benches that were
    freshly painted to ones that weren't,
And when he finally did marry a girl who made his pulses
    quicken
It was merely because her name was Gale Winterbottom
    and she was no spring chicken,
And one day during the worm-warning season he came
    home hungry after a hard day in the stirrup,
And she served him waffles and he objected to the May-
    pole syrup,
So she shot him through the heart, but his last words were
    ecstatic.
He said Thank you honey, it was thoughtful of you to use
    the autumnatic.


## MARTHA'S VINEYARD

I live at the top of old West Chop
In a house with a cranky stove,
And when I swim I risk life and limb
On the pebbles that line the cove —
Where the waves wish-wash, and the foghorn blows,
And the blowfish nibble at your toes-oes-oes,
The blowfish nibble at your toes.

[   86   ]

I lunch and sup on schrod and scup,
And once in a while on beans,
And the only news that I get to peruse
Is in last year's magazines —
Where the waves wish-wash, and the foghorn blows,
And the blowfish nibble at your toes-oes-oes,
The blowfish nibble at your toes.

When the sea gulls shout the lights go out,
And whenever the lights go on
I pursue the moth with a dusting cloth
Till the Bob White brings the dawn —
Where the waves wish-wash, and the foghorn blows,
And the blowfish nibble at your toes-oes-oes,
The blowfish nibble at your toes.

But when the breeze creeps through the trees
And the wee waves shiver and shake,
Oh, I wouldn't swap my old West Chop
For a sizzling Western steak —
I want to wish-wash where the foghorn blows,
And the blowfish nibble at your toes-oes-oes,
The blowfish nibble at your toes.


## TWO DOGS HAVE I

For years we've had a little dog,
Last year we acquired a big dog;
He wasn't big when we got him,
He was littler than the dog we had.
We thought our little dog would love him,
Would help him to become a trig dog,

[ 87 ]

But the new little dog got bigger,
And the old little dog got mad.

Now the big dog loves the little dog,
But the little dog hates the big dog,
The little dog is eleven years old,
And the big dog only one;
The little dog calls him *Schweinhund*,
The little dog calls him Pig-dog,
She grumbles broken curses
As she dreams in the August sun.

The big dog's teeth are terrible,
But he wouldn't bite the little dog;
The little dog would grind his spine,
But the little dog has no teeth;
The big dog is acrobatic,
The little dog is a brittle dog;
She leaps to grip his jugular,
And passes underneath.

The big dog clings to the little dog
Like glue and cement and mortar;
The little dog is his own true love;
But the big dog is to her
Like a scarlet rag to a Longhorn,
Or a suitcase to a porter;
The day he sat on the hornet
I distinctly heard her purr.

Well, how can you blame the little dog,
Who was once the household darling?

He romps like a young Adonis,
She droops like an old mustache;
No wonder she steals his corner,
No wonder she comes out snarling,
No wonder she calls him *Cochon*
And even *Espèce de vache.*

Yet once I wanted a sandwich,
Either caviar or cucumber,
When the sun had not yet risen
And the moon had not yet sank;
As I tiptoed through the hallway
The big dog lay in slumber,
And the little dog slept by the big dog,
And her head was on his flank.


### EDOUARD

A bugler named Dougal MacDougal
Found ingenious ways to be frugal.
He learned how to sneeze
In various keys,
Thus saving the price of a bugle.

## A WORD ABOUT WINTER

Now the frost is on the pane,
Rugs upon the floor again,
Now the screens are in the cellar,
Now the student cons the speller,
Lengthy summer noon is gone,
Twilight treads the heels of dawn,
Round-eyed sun is now a squinter,
Tiptoe breeze a panting sprinter,
Every cloud a blizzard hinter,
Squirrel on the snow a printer,
Rain spout sprouteth icy splinter,
Willy-nilly, this is winter.

Summer-swollen doorjambs settle,
Ponds and puddles turn to metal,
Skater whoops in frisky fettle,
Golf-club stingeth like a nettle,
Radiator sings like kettle,
Hearth is popocatapetl.

Runneth nose and chappeth lip,
Draft evadeth weather strip,
Doctor wrestleth with grippe
In never-ending rivalship.
Rosebush droops in garden shoddy,
Blood is cold and thin in body,
Weary postman dreams of toddy,
Head before the hearth grows noddy.

On the hearth the embers gleam,
Glowing like a maiden's dream,
Now the apple and the oak
Paint the sky with chimney smoke,
Husband now, without disgrace,
Dumps ash trays in the fireplace.


## WHEN YOU SAY THAT, SMILE!
### or
## ALL RIGHT THEN, DON'T SMILE

When the odds are long,
And the game goes wrong,
Does your *joie de vivre* diminish?
Have you little delight

[ 91 ]

In an uphill fight?
Do you wince at a Garrison finish?
Then here's my hand, my trusty partner!
I've always wanted a good disheartener.

*Oh, things are frequently what they seem,*
*And this is wisdom's crown:*
*Only the game fish swims upstream,*
*But the sensible fish swims down.*

Well, how is your pulse
When a cad insults
The lady you're cavaliering?
Are you willing to wait
To retaliate
Till the cad is out of hearing?
Then here's my hand, my trusty companion,
And may neither one of us fall in a canyon.

*For things are frequently what they seem,*
*And this is wisdom's crown:*
*Only the game fish swims upstream,*
*But the sensible fish swims down.*

## THE FACTS OF LIFE

Daughter, dim those reverent eyes;
Daddy must apologize.
Daddy's not an engineer;
Never will be, now, I fear.
Daddy couldn't drive a train,
Not for all the sherry in Spain.

Daddy's not a fireman, too;
He couldn't do what firemen do.
Clanging bells and screaming sirens
Are no part of his environs.
In case of fire, no hero he;
Merely a humble rescuee.

Also, greatly to his grief,
Daddy's not an Indian chief.
Daddy cannot stealthy walk
Or wield a lethal tomahawk.
Hark to Daddy's secret grim:
Feathers only tickle him.

Better learn it now than later:
Daddy's not an aviator.
Daddy cannot soar and swoop,
Neither can he loop the loop.
Parachutes he never hung on to,
And what is worse, he doesn't want to.

As long as Daddy's being defiant,
Daddy, child, is not a giant.
You'll travel far if you would seek
A less remarkable physique.
That's why he feels a decade older
When you are riding on his shoulder.

Another thing that Daddy ain't,
I frankly tell you, is a saint.
Daddy, my faithful catechumen,
Is widely known as all too human.

Still, if you watch him, you will find
He does his best, when so inclined.

One final skeleton while I dare:
Daddy's not a millionaire.
Alas, his most amusing verse
Is not a Fortunatus purse.
What I should buy for you, my sweeting,
Did journals end in both ends meeting!

There, child, you have the dismal truth,
Now obvious as a missing tooth.
Your doom it is to be the daughter
Of one as romantic as soapy water.
Should you like it, you'd overwhelm me,
And if you hate it, please don't tell me.


## KINDLY UNHITCH THAT STAR, BUDDY

I hardly suppose I know anybody who wouldn't rather be
a success than a failure,
Just as I suppose every piece of crabgrass in the garden
would much rather be an azalea,
And in celestial circles all the run-of-the-mill angels would
rather be archangels or at least cherubim and seraphim,
And in the legal world all the little process-servers hope
to grow up into great big bailiffim and sheriffim.
Indeed, everybody wants to be a wow,
But not everybody knows exactly how.
Some people think they will eventually wear diamonds in-
stead of rhinestones

Only by everlastingly keeping their noses to their ghrine-
    stones,
And other people think they will be able to put in more
    time at Palm Beach and the Ritz
By not paying too much attention to hard work but rather
    in being brilliant by starts and fits.
In short, the world is filled with people trying to achieve
    success,
And half of them think they'll get it by saying No and
    half of them by saying Yes,
And if all the ones who say No said Yes, and vice versa,
    such is the fate of humanity that ninety-nine per cent
    of them still wouldn't be any better off than they were
    before,
Which perhaps is just as well because if everybody was a
    success nobody could be contemptuous of anybody else
    and everybody would start in all over again trying to
    be a bigger success than everybody else so they would
    have somebody to be contemptuous of and so on for-
    evermore,
Because when people start hitching their wagons to a star,
That's the way they are.


## THE PASSIONATE PAGAN AND THE
## DISPASSIONATE PUBLIC

A TRAGEDY OF THE MACHINE AGE

Boys and girls,
Come out to play,
The moon is shining
Bright as day.

*If the moon is shining*
*Bright as day,*
*We think that we'll*
*Stay in and play.*

Hey nonny nonny!
Come, Jennie! Come, Johnnie!
The year's adolescent!
The air's effervescent!
It bubbles like Schweppes!
Aren't you going to take steppes?

*It's one of the commoner*
*Vernal phenomena.*
*You may go wild*
*Over air that is mild,*
*But Johnnie and Jennie*
*Are not having any.*

It is Spring! It is Spring!
Let us leap! Let us sing!
Let us claim we have hives
And abandon our wives!
Let us hire violins
And pin flowers on our skins!
Let us loll in a grotto!
Let this be our motto:
Not sackcloth, but satin!
Not Nordic, but Latin!

*A radio voice*
*Is our amorous choice!*

*Tell us that Luna*
*Compares with that cruna.*
*Away with your capers!*
*Go peddle your papers!*

It is Spring! It is Spring!
On the lea, on the ling!
The frost is dispersed!
Like the buds let us burst!
Let the sap in our veins
Rush like limited trains,
While Bacchus and Pan
Cavort in the van!

*Spring is what winter*
*Always goes inter.*
*Science finds reasons*
*For mutable seasons.*
*Can't you control*
*That faun in your soul?*
*Please go and focus*
*Your whims on a crocus.*

It is Spring! Is it Spring?
Let us sing! Shall we sing?
On the lea, on the ling
Shall we sing it is Spring?
Will nobody fling
A garland to Spring?
Oh, hey nonny nonny!
Oh, Jennie! Oh, Johnnie!

Doesn't dove rhyme with love
While the moon shines above?
Isn't May for the wooer
And June for *l'amour?*
No, it couldn't be Spring!
Do not dance! Do not sing!
These birds and these flowers,
These breezes and bowers,
These gay tirra-lirras
Are all done with mirrors!
Hey nonny! Hey nonny!
Hey nonny! Hey nonny!
Hey nonny! Hey nonny!
Hey nonny . . .

## TWO AND ONE ARE A PROBLEM

Dear Miss Dix, you have helped a love lorn friend of mine
    twice,
So I turn to you for advice.
You see, it started when I was away on the road
And returned to find a pair of lovebirds had taken up their
    residence in my abode.
Well I am not crazy about lovebirds, but I must say they
    looked very sweet in their gilded cage,
And their friendship had reached an advanced stage,
And I had just forgiven her who of the feathered fiancé
    was the donor of
When the children caught a lost lovebird in the yard that
    we couldn't locate the owner of.
So then we had three, and it was no time for flippancy,
Because everybody knows that a lovebird without its own

lovebird to love will pine away and die of the dis-
    crepancy,
So we bought a fourth lovebird for the third lovebird and
    they sat around very cozily beak to beak
And then the third lovebird that we had provided the
    fourth lovebird for to keep it from dying died at
    the end of the week,
So we were left with an odd lovebird and it was no time
    for flippancy,
Because a lovebird without its own lovebird to love will
    pine away and die of the discrepancy,
So we had to buy a fifth lovebird to console the fourth
    lovebird that we had bought to keep the third lovebird
    contented,
And now the fourth lovebird has lost its appetite, and
    Miss Dix, I am going demented.
I don't want to break any hearts, but I got to know where
    I'm at;
Must I keep on buying lovebirds, Miss Dix, or do you think
    it would be all right to buy a cat?


## DRAGONS ARE TOO SELDOM

To actually see an actual marine monster
Is one of the things that do before I die I wonster.
Should you ask me if I desire to meet the bashful inhabit-
    ant of Loch Ness,
I could only say yes.
Often my eye with moisture dims
When I think that it has never been my good fortune to
    gaze on one of Nature's whims.

Far from ever having seen a Gorgon
I haven't even seen the midget that sat in the lap of Mr.
    Morgan.
Indeed it is my further ill fortune or mishap
That far from having seen the midget that sat in it I have
    never even seen Mr. Morgan's lap.
Indeed I never much thought about Mr. Morgan's having
    a lap because just the way you go into churches and
    notice the stained glass more than the apses
When you think about multi-millionaires you don't think
    about their laps as much as their lapses;
But it seems that they do have laps which is one human
    touch that brings them a little closer to me and you,
And maybe they even go so far as to sometimes have hiccups
    too.
But regular monsters like sea serpents don't have laps or
    hiccups or any other characteristic that is human,
And I would rather see a second-rate monster such as a
    mermaid than a first-rate genius such as John Bunyan
    or Schiaparelli or Schubert or Schumann;
Yes, I would rather see one of the sirens
Than two Lord Byrons,
And if I knew that when I got there I could see Cyclops
    or Scylla and Charybdis or Pegasus
I would willingly walk on my hands from here to Dallas,
    Tegasus,
Because I don't mean to be satirical,
But where there's a monster there's a miracle,
And after a thorough study of current affairs, I have con-
    cluded with regret
That the world can profitably use all the miracles it can
    get,

And I think life would be a lot less demoralizing,
If instead of sitting around in front of the radio listening
    to torture singers sing torture songs we sat around
    listening to the Lorelei loreleising.

## A WARNING TO WIVES

"The outcome of the trial is another warning that if you must
kill someone, you should spare the person possessing life insurance. . . . Figures are available to show that convictions are
much more common in 'insurance murders' than in other types
of homicides." — BOSTON HERALD.

Speak gently to your husband, ma'am,
And encourage all his sneezes;
That nasty cough may carry him off,
If exposed to drafts and breezes.
But suppose the scoundrel lingers on,
And insists on being cured;
Well, it isn't a sin if a girl steps in —
Unless the brute's insured.

Oh, the selfishness of men, welladay, welladay!
Oh the sissies, oh the softies, oh the mice!
Egotistically they strive to keep themselves alive,
And insurance is their scurviest device.
Insurance!
It's insurance
That tries a lady's temper past endurance.
Yet it's safer, on the whole,
To practice self-control
If there's apt to be a question of insurance.

Arsenic soup is a dainty soup,
But not if he's paid his premium.
Or a .32 in a pinch will do,
If you're bored with the epithalemium.
But to make acquittal doubly sure —
No maybes, no perhapses —
You'll do well to wait to expunge your mate
Until his policy lapses.


The hypocrisy of men, welladay, welladay!
Whited sepulchers are much to be preferred.
They claim it's for their wives they evaluate their lives,
But it's fatal if you take them at their word.
Insurance!
Oh, insurance!
What holds potential widows fast in durance?
Not the Adlers and the Freuds,
But the Mutuals and Lloyds,
And the jury's evil mind about insurance.


## HUSH, HERE THEY COME

Some people get savage and bitter when to backbiters they
    refer,
But I just purr.
Yes, some people consider backbiters to be rankest of the
    rank,
But frankly, I prefer them to people who go around being
    frank,

Because usually when you are backbitten behind your back
   you don't know about it and it doesn't leave a trace,
But frankness consists of having your back bitten right to
   your face,
And as if that weren't enough to scar you,
Why you are right there in person to scotch the defama-
   tion, and if you don't happen to be able to scotch it,
   why where are you?
Frank people are grim, but genuine backbiters are delight-
   ful to have around,
Because they are so anxious that if what they have been
   saying about you has reached your ears you shouldn't
   believe it, that they are the most amiable companions
   to be found;
They will entertain you from sunset to dawn,
And cater encouragingly to all your weaknesses so that they
   can broadcast them later on,
So what if they do gnaw on your spine after enjoying your
   beer and skittles?
I don't blame them the least of jots or tittles,
Because certainly no pastime such diversion lends
As talking friends over analytically with friends,
So what if as they leave your house or you leave theirs
   backbiters strip your flesh and your clothes off,
At least it is your back that they bite, and not your nose off.
I believe in a place for everything and everything in its
   place,
And I don't care how unkind the things people say about
   me so long as they don't say them to my face.

# ARE YOU A SNODGRASS?

It is possible that most individual and international social
and economic collisions
Result from humanity's being divided into two main divi-
sions,
Both of which are irreconcilable,
And neither is by the other beguilable;
Their lives are spent in mutual interference,
And yet you cannot tell them apart by their outward ap-
pearance.
Indeed the only way in which to tell one group from the
other you are able
Is to observe them at the table,
Because the only visible way in which one group from the
other varies
Is in its treatment of the cream and sugar on cereal and
berries.
Group A, which we will call the Swozzlers because it is
a very suitable name, I deem,
First applies the sugar and then swozzles it all over the
place pouring on the cream,
And as fast as they put the sugar on they swozzle it
away,
But such thriftlessness means nothing to ruthless egotists
like they,
They just continue to scoop and swozzle and swozzle and
scoop,
Until there is nothing left for the Snodgrasses, or second
group.
A Snodgrass is a kind, handsome intelligent person who
pours the cream on first,

And then deftly sprinkles the sugar over the cereal or berries
after they have been properly immersed,

Thus assuring himself that the sugar will remain on the
cereal and berries where it can do some good, which
is his wish,

Instead of being swozzled away to the bottom of the
dish.

The facts of the case for the Snodgrasses are so self-evident
that it is ridiculous to debate them,

But this is unfortunate for the Snodgrasses as it only causes
the sinister and vengeful Swozzlers all the more to
hate them.

Swozzlers are irked by the superior Snodgrass intelligence
and nobility

And they lose no opportunity of inflicting on them every
kind of incivility.

If you read that somebody has been run over by an auto-
mobile

You may be sure that the victim was a Snodgrass, and a
Swozzler was at the wheel.

Swozzlers start wars and Snodgrasses get killed in them,

Swozzlers sell water-front lots and Snodgrasses get malaria
when they try to build in them.

Swozzlers invent fashionable diets and drive Snodgrasses
crazy with tables of vitamins and calories,

Swozzlers go to Congress and think up new taxes and
Snodgrasses pay their salaries,

Swozzlers bring tigers back alive and Snodgrasses get eaten
by anacondas,

Snodgrasses are depositors and Swozzlers are absconders,

Swozzlers hold straight flushes when Snodgrasses hold four
of a kind,

Swozzlers step heavily on the toes of Snodgrasses' shoes as
 soon as they are shined.
Whatever achievements Snodgrasses achieve, Swozzlers al-
 ways top them;
Snodgrasses say Stop me if you've heard this one, and
 Swozzlers stop them.
Swozzlers are teeming with useful tricks of the trade that
 are not included in standard university curricula;
The world in general is their oyster, and Snodgrasses in
 particular.
So I hope for your sake, dear reader, that you are a Swozzler,
 but I hope for everybody else's sake that you are not,
And I also wish that everybody else was a nice amiable
 Snodgrass too, because then life would be just one
 long sweet harmonious mazurka or gavotte.

### THE STRANGE CASE OF MR. DONNYBROOK'S
### BOREDOM

Once upon a time there was a man named Mr. Donnybrook.
He was married to a woman Mrs. Donnybrook.
Mr. and Mrs. Donnybrook dearly loved to be bored.
Sometimes they were bored at the ballet, other times at the
 cinema.
They were bored riding elephants in India and elevators in
 the Empire State Building.
They were bored by Grand Dukes and garbagemen, deb-
 utantes and demimondaines, opera singers and opera-
 tions.

They scoured the Five Continents and the Seven Seas in their mad pursuit of boredom.

This went on for years and years.

One day Mr. Donnybrook turned to Mrs. Donnybrook.

My dear, he said, we have reached the end of our rope.

We have exhausted every yawn.

The world holds nothing more to jade our titillated palates.

Well, said Mrs. Donnybrook, we might try insomnia.

So they tried insomnia.

About two o'clock the next morning Mr. Donnybrook said, My, insomnia is certainly quite boring, isn't it?

Mrs. Donnybrook said it certainly was, wasn't it?

Mr. Donnybrook said it certainly was.

Pretty soon he began to count sheep.

Mrs. Donnybrook began to count sheep, too.

After a while Mr. Donnybrook said, Hey, you're counting my sheep!

Stop counting my sheep, said Mr. Donnybrook.

Why, the very idea, said Mrs. Donnybrook.

I guess I know my own sheep, don't I?

How? said Mr. Donnybrook.

They're cattle, said Mrs. Donnybrook.

They're cattle, and longhorns at that.

Furthermore, said Mrs. Donnybrook, us cattle ranchers is shore tired o' you sheepmen plumb ruinin' our water.

I give yuh fair warnin', said Mrs. Donnybrook, yuh better get them woolly Gila monsters o' yourn back across the Rio Grande afore mornin' or I'm a goin' to string yuh up on the nearest cottonwood.

Carramba! sneered Mr. Donnybrook. Thees ees free range, no?

No, said Mrs. Donnybrook, not for sheep men.
She strung him up on the nearest cottonwood.
Mr. Donnybrook had never been so bored in his life.


### FAHRENHEIT GESUNDHEIT

Nothing is glummer
Than a cold in the summer.
A summer cold
Is to have and to hold.
A cough in the fall
Is nothing at all,
A winter snuffle
Is lost in the shuffle,
And April sneezes
Put leaves on the treeses,
But a summer cold
Is to have and to hold.
Though golf course and beach
Slip beyond your reach,
By a fate grotesque
You can get to your desk,
And there is no rescue
From this germ grotesque.
You can feel it coming
In your nasal plumbing,
But there is no plumber
For a cold in the summer.
Nostrilly, tonsilly,
It prowls irresponsilly;
In your personal firmament

Its abode is permamant.
Oh, would it were curable
Rather than durable;
Were it Nero's or Himmler's,
Or somebody similar's!
O Stalin, were it thine!
But it isn't, it's mine.
A summer cold
Is to have and to hold.

## A CLEAN CONSCIENCE NEVER RELAXES

There is an emotion to which we are most of us adduced.
But it is one which I refuse to boost.
It is harrowing, browbeating, and brutal,
Besides which it is futile.
Because of it sleepy men go sleepless,

Because of it, for all I know lyrical canaries and night-
　　ingales go peepless;
Hungry men lose their appetites;
Warm acrobats perspire coldly in their dapper tights;
Eligible bachelors enter ballrooms less eligibly,
And stoics talk to themselves loudly but fortunately also
　　unintelligibly.
Land of Goshen,
What an easily dispensable emotion!
I am referring, of course,
To remorse.
Remorse is a violent dyspepsia of the mind,
But it is very difficult to treat because it cannot even be
　　defined,
Because everything is not gold that glisters and everything
　　is not a tear that glistens,
And one man's remorse is another man's reminiscence,
So the truth is that as far as improving the world is con-
　　cerned, remorse is a duffer,
Because the wrong people suffer,
Because the very fact that they suffer from remorse proves
　　they are innocuous,
Yes indeed, it is the man remorse passes over completely
　　who is the virulent streptococcuous.
Do you think that when Nero threw a martyr to the lions
　　remorse enveloped him like an affinity?
Why, the only remorse in the whole Colosseum was felt
　　by the martyr who was reproaching himself for having
　　dozed through the sermon on the second Sunday after
　　Trinity.
So I think remorse ought to stop biting the consciences that
　　feed it,

And I think the Communist Party ought to work out some
plan for taking it away from those who have it and
giving it to those who need it.

## IT'S SNUG TO BE SMUG

Oh, sometimes I wish I had the wings of an angel because
then I could fly through the air with the greatest of
ease,

And if I wanted to be somewhere else I could get there
without spending any money on taxis or railroad
tickets or tips or fees,

Yes, I could fly to Paris and do as a Parisian, or fly to Rome
and do as a Roman,

But on the other hand wings would necessitate my sleeping on my abdomen,

So I don't really wish I had the wings of an angel, but
sometimes I wish I had the sweet voice of a thrush,

And then if I sang an Indian Love Lyric why thousands
of beautiful beauties would harken and quiver and
blush,

And it would be a treat to hear my rendition of Sweet Alice
Ben Bolt,

But on the other hand who would go to harken to anybody
who was known to eat insects and moult?

So I don't really wish I had the sweet voice of a thrush,
but sometimes I wish I had the courage of a lion,

And then I could look life in the eye with a will of iron,

And to a goose, or a burglar, or even a butler, I wouldn't
hesitate to say Boo!

But on the other hand I might encounter a goose or a bur-
    glar or a butler who had the courage of a lion too,
So I don't really wish I had the courage of a lion but some-
    times I wish I had an elephant's muscle,
And then when somebody fainted or got run over I could
    always get in the front row of spectators no matter
    how thick the hustle and bustle,
But on the other hand I would probably find myself in
    some job where such strength would be utilitarian,
So if I had the muscle of an elephant, why instead of
    lying back comfortably and wishing I had the muscle
    of an elephant, why I would probably be busy build-
    ing a tower in Manhattan or tunneling through a peak
    in Darian,
So I don't really wish I had the muscle of an elephant but
    sometimes I wish I had the innocence of a lamb,
And then I would never wake up crying Fie on me! What
    an un-innocent sinner I am!
But on the other hand innocence is a security on which
    it is hard to borrow,
Because all it means is that either you get eaten by a wolf
    today or else the shepherd saves you from the wolf
    so he can sell you to the butcher tomorrow,
So I do not really wish I had the innocence of a lamb,
I guess I'll stay just as I am.


### THE LIFE OF THE PARTY

Lily, there isn't a thing you lack,
Your effect is simply stunning.
But Lily, your gown is low in the back,

So conduct yourself with cunning.
Some of your charm is charm of face,
But some of your charm is spinal;
Losing your looks is no disgrace,
But losing your poise is final.
Ridicule's name is Legion,
So look to your dorsal region.

For Artie,
Old Artie,
The life of the party,
Is practically perfect tonight;
He's high as the nose of a kite;
He's never appeared so bright.
Have you ever seen Artie
Enliven a party?
You've never seen Artie —
Why Lord love a duck!
At present old Artie is running amuck.
There's a wink in his eye
And a smile on his lips
For the matron he tickles,
The waiter he trips.
There's a rubber cigar,
And an un-funny jest,
To melt the reserve
Of the clerical guest.
There's a pin for the man who stoops over,
And a little trained flea for Rover.
So Lily, beware of your back!
More daring than duller and older blades,
Artie is hot on the track.

[ 114 ]

I've noticed him eying your shoulderblades.
And maybe it's salad,
And maybe it's ice,
But I fear he has planned
Some amusing device,
For the laughter is slack
And he's taking it hard —
He's eying your back —
And Artie's a card —
He's forming a plan —
May I fetch you a shawl?
That inventive young man —
There is one in the hall.
Though your back is divine
In its natural state,
May I curtain your spine? —
*Dear Heaven, I'm late!*
Aren't you glad that you came to the party?
And weren't you amused by Artie?

Horace, the moment that you appeared,
I admired your manly beauty,
But I feel that a word about your beard
Is only my bounden duty.
Your tailor's craft is a dandy's dream,
Your suavity leaves me lyrical,
But escaping tonight with your self-esteem
Will require a minor miracle.
Fun is a gay deceiver,
So look to your kingly beaver.
For Artie,
Old Artie,

The life of the party,
Is hitting his stride tonight.
No bushel obscures his light.
He's knocking them left and right.
Have you ever seen Artie
Enliven a party?
You've never seen Artie —
My lad, you're in luck,
For Artie, old Artie, is running amuck.
At Artie's approach
Lesser wags droop.
Have you seen the tin roach
He drops in your soup?
Is a spoon in your pocket?
Or gum in your chair?
It's Artie, old Artie,
Who magicked them there.
And of those who complain, there's a rumor
That they're lacking in sense of humor.
So Horace, beware of your beard!
I scent some fantastic flubdubbery!
Old Artie has just disappeared
And I've noticed him eying your shrubbery.
And maybe it's syrup,
And maybe it's mice,
But I fear he has planned
Some amusing device.
His conceptions are weird,
And nothing is barred —
He was eying your beard —
And Artie's a card —
When Artie returns,

The fun will begin —
May I fetch you a bag
To put on your chin?
Just a small paper bag
To envelop the bait?
For Artie's a wag —
*Dear Heaven, I'm late!*
Aren't you glad that you came to the party?
And weren't you amused by Artie?


## UNANSWERED BY REQUEST

There are several things in life that keep me guessing,
And one of them is what are the French words for French
  leave and French fried potatoes and French dressing,
And I am also a trifle vague
About how you ask people to a Dutch treat or talk to them
  like a Dutch uncle in The Hague.
And why do restaurants put signs in their windows ad-
  vertising REAL HOME COOKING and expect the
  customers to come rushing in all panting and over-
  joyed
When the reason that half the people who eat in restaurants are eating in restaurants is because with home
  cooking they have become cloyed?
And when is a violin a fiddle?
And when the tide goes out here does it go in some where
  else or does it just pile up and make the ocean deeper
  in the middle?

And who is the brownie whose duty it is to see that the
  theater curtain never goes up on time except the one
  evening that you are late?
And who is the railroad dispatcher who arranges his dis-
  patching so that every time you are about to see something interesting out of your train window your view
  is cut off by a hundred-car freight?
All these moot questions and many others equally moot if
  not even mooter
Must be faced by every thinking male and female practically as soon as they graduate from their kiddiecar
  or scooter,
Because they are the kind of riddles and conundrums with
  which life
Is far too too rife,
But fortunately for the human race thinking people eventually discover that there is only one satisfactory way
  of dealing with a riddle or a conundrum.
And that is to stop worrying about the answers and just
  get clean out from undrum.

## DRIVE SLOW, MAN CHORTLING

Gangway, everybody, hold your hats,
Curb your dogs and leash your cats,
Embrace your young in parental clasp,
Breathe in deep and prepare to gasp,
Feel your pulse grow rapid and joggly,
Open your eyes and goggle agogly,
Hitch your wonderment to a star —
Here comes me in a brand-new car.

Behold this gem of automobiles!
At either end it has two wheels.
What's more, you'll notice as you draw near it
Another wheel inside, to steer it.
Oh my, how I that car admires!
The outside wheels have rubber tires.
Oh bless the day that I was born!
The inside wheel supports the horn.

My natal day I will not curse.
I've three speeds forward and one reverse.
The backward speed I truly adore,
Yet love the forward three times more.
Upon this car I am a doter;
Golly, it's even got a motor!
Nothing so much a car improves
As when you start it up, it moves.

Pour forth, my soul, in joyous hymns;
The wiper wipes, the dimmer dims,
The body on loving springs is bolstered,
And wherever you sit, it's all upholstered.
The luggage compartment is so commodious
That sleeping in it would not be odious.
Doubt if you must, but I know I'm right, there;
As a matter of fact, I spent last night there.

Oh how I pity Father Divine,
Who hasn't a new car just like mine.
Kings and emperors make mistakes
Riding around in inferior makes.
Gangway, you motoring proletariat,
Here comes me in a brand-new chariot,
And I'll sell you my thoughts for one half of tuppence:
A lot of road hogs are going to get their come-uppance.

## WHERE THERE'S A WILL, THERE'S
## VELLEITY

Seated one day at the dictionary I was pretty weary and
    also pretty ill at ease,

Because a word I had always liked turned out not to be a
    word at all, and suddenly I found myself among
    the v's,

And suddenly among the v's I came across a new word
    which was a word called *velleity,*

So the new word I found was better than the old word I
    lost, for which I thank my tutelary deity,

Because velleity is a word which gives me great satisfac-
    tion,

Because do you know what it means, it means *low degree
of volition not prompting to action,*

And I always knew I had something holding me back but
    I didn't know what,

And it's quite a relief to know it isn't a conspiracy, it's only
    velleity that I've got,

Because to be wonderful at everything has always been my
    ambition,

Yes indeed, I am simply teeming with volition,

So why I never was wonderful at anything was something
    I couldn't see

While all the time, of course, my volition was merely voli-
    tion of a low degree,

Which is the kind of volition that you are better off with-
    out it,

Because it puts an idea in your head but doesn't prompt
    you to do anything about it.

[ 121 ]

So you think it would be nice to be a great pianist but why
     bother with practicing for hours at the keyboard,
Or you would like to be the romantic captain of a romantic
     ship but can't find time to study navigation or charts
     of the ocean or the seaboard;
You want a lot of money but you are not prepared to work
     for it,
Or a book to read in bed but you do not care to go into
     the nocturnal cold and murk for it;
And now if you have any such symptoms you can identify
     your malady with accurate spontaneity:
It's velleity,
So don't forget to remember that you're velleitous, and if
     anybody says you're just lazy,
Why, they're crazy.

## THE MIND OF PROFESSOR PRIMROSE

My story begins in the town of Cambridge, Mass.,
Home of the Harvard Business and Dental Schools,
And more or less the home of Harvard College.
Now, Harvard is a cultural institution,
Squandering many a dollar upon professors,
Professors wise and prowling in search of wisdom,
And every mother's son of them absent-minded.
But the absentest mind belonged to Professor Primrose.
He had won a Nobel award and a Pulitzer Prize,
A Guggenheim and a leg on the Davis Cup,
But he couldn't remember to shave both sides of his face.
He frequently lit his hair and combed his cigar;
He set a trap for the baby and dandled the mice;

He wound up his key and opened the door with his watch;
He fed the mosquitoes crumbs and slapped at the robins;
He always said his prayers when he entered the theater,
And left the church for a smoke between the act;
He gave the exterminator man a cookie
And told his guests to go way, he had no bugs;
He rode the streets on a bicycle built for two,
And he never discovered he wasn't teaching at Yale.
At last one summer he kissed his crimson flannels
And packed his wife in camphor, and she complained.
She had always hated camphor, and she complained.
"My dear," she ordered, "these *contretemps* must cease;
You must bring this wandering mind a little bit nearer;
You must tidy up that disorderly cerebellum;
You must write today and enroll in the Pelman Institute.
The Pelman people will cure your absent mind."
He embraced his pen and he took his wife in hand,
He wrinkled a stamp and thoughtfully licked his brow,
He wrote the letter and mailed it, and what do you know?
In a couple of days he disappeared from Cambridge.
"For heaven's sake, my husband has disappeared,"
Said Mrs. Primrose. "Now isn't that just like him?"
And she cut the meat and grocery orders in half,
And moved the chairs in the living room around,
And settled down to a little solid comfort.
She had a marvelous time for seven years,
At the end of which she took a train to Chicago.
She liked to go to Chicago once in a while
Because of a sister-in-law who lived in Cambridge.
Her eye was caught at Schenectady by the porter;
She noticed that he was brushing off a dime,
And trying to put the passenger in his pocket.

"Porter," she said, "aren't you Professor Primrose?
Aren't you my husband, the missing Professor Primrose?
And what did you learn at the Pelman Institute?"
"Mah Lawd, Maria," the porter said, "mah Lawd!
Did you say *Pelman?* Ah wrote to de *Pullman* folks!"

## SPRING COMES TO BALTIMORE
### or
## CHRISTMAS COMES MORE PROMPTLY

Whatever others may sing of spring,
I wish to sing there is no such thing.
Spring is simply a seasonal gap
When winter and summer overlap.
What kind of a system is it, please,
When in March you parch, and in May you freeze?
Yet give some people a glimpse of a crocus,
And all their perspective gets out of focus.
They lose their rubbers and store their V-necks,
And omit to renew their supply of Kleenex,
They shed their ulsters to walk uphill in,
And forget their sulfa and penicillin.
I suppose it's the same in Patagonia;
Today spring fever, tomorrow pneumonia.

Yes, others may sing in praise of spring,
I wish to sing there is no such thing.
Spring is a phantom, spring is a fraud,
I shall not, will not be overawed.
What if a puddle or two has thawed,
And the kittenish zephyr is velvet-pawed,

[ 125 ]

And the day is long as the night is broad,
And the robins approve and the frogs applaud,
And lovers haste to get mother-in-lawed?
I still refuse to be overawed —
Except when the clouds drift light as gossamer,
When the dogwood progresses from blossom to blossomer,
And the song of the possum is nightly possumer;
Except when the rivulet sings like a dulcimer,
And the bill of fare is daily fulsomer;
When the succulent roe consoles the shad
For the offspring it never got to have had;
And the soft-shell crab finds a homey billet,
Snuggling down in a cozy skillet.

Let others refuse to sing of spring,
I wish to sing it's a splendid thing.
Let others of diet be particular,
Existing pallid and perpendicular;
We're rosy as pippins and twice as circular,
Not perpendicular, but pippindercular.
Such is spring on the generous Chesapeake,
Where recipes reach their springtime recipeake.


## MR. ARTESIAN'S CONSCIENTIOUSNESS

Once there was a man named Mr. Artesian and his activity
	was tremendous,
And he grudged every minute away from his desk because
	the importance of his work was so stupendous;
And he had one object all sublime,
Which was to save simply oodles of time.

He figured that sleeping eight hours a night meant that
    if he lived to be seventy-five he would have spent
    twenty-five years not at his desk but in bed,
So he cut his slumber to six hours which meant he only
    lost eighteen years and nine months instead,
And he figured that taking ten minutes for breakfast and
    twenty minutes for luncheon and half an hour for
    dinner meant that he spent three years, two months
    and fifteen days at the table,
So that by subsisting solely on bouillon cubes which he
    swallowed at his desk to save this entire period he
    was able,
And he figured that at ten minutes a day he spent a little
    over six months and ten days shaving,
So he grew a beard, which gave him a considerable saving,
And you might think that now he might have been satis-
    fied, but no, he wore a thoughtful frown,
Because he figured that at two minutes a day he would
    spend thirty-eight days and a few minutes in ele-
    vators just traveling up and down,
So as a final timesaving device he stepped out the win-
    dow of his office, which happened to be on the
    fiftieth floor,
And one of his partners asked "Has he vertigo?" and the
    other glanced out and down and said "Oh no, only
    about ten feet more."


## A BULLETIN HAS JUST COME IN

The rabbit's dreamy eyes grow dreamier
As he quietly gives you tularemia.

The parrot clashes his hooked proboscis
And laughs while handing you psittacosis.

In every swamp or wooded area
Mosquito witches brew malaria.

We risk at every jolly picnic
Spotted fever from a tick nick.

People perish of bubonic;
To rats, it's better than a tonic.

The hog converted into pork
Puts trichinosis on your fork.

The dog today that guards your babies
Tomorrow turns and gives them rabies.

The baby, once all milk and spittle,
Grows to a Hitler, and boy, can he hittle!

That's our planet, and we're stuck with it.
I wish its inheritors the best of luck with it.


## WILL CONSIDER SITUATION

These here are words of radical advice for a young man
    looking for a job;
Young man, be a snob.

Yes, if you are in search of arguments against starting at the bottom,
Why I've gottom.
Let the personnel managers differ;
It's obvious that you will get on faster at the top than at the bottom because there are more people at the bottom than at the top so naturally the competition at the bottom is stiffer.
If you need any further proof that my theory works,
Well, nobody can deny that presidents get paid more than vice-presidents and vice-presidents get paid more than clerks.
Stop looking at me quizzically;
I want to add that you will never achieve fortune in a job that makes you uncomfortable physically.
When anybody tells you that hard jobs are better for you than soft jobs be sure to repeat this text to them,
Postmen tramp around all day through rain and snow just to deliver people in cozy air-conditioned offices checks to them.
You don't need to interpret tea leaves stuck in a cup
To understand that people who work sitting down get paid more than people who work standing up.
Another thing about having a comfortable job is you not only accumulate more treasure;
You get more leisure.
So that when you find you have worked so comfortably that your waistline is a menace,
You correct it with golf or tennis.
Whereas if in an uncomfortable job like piano-moving or stevedoring you indulge,
You have no time for exercise, you just continue to bulge.

To sum it up, young man, there is every reason to refuse
    a job that will make heavy demands on you corporally
    or manually,
And the only intelligent way to start your career is to ac-
    cept a sitting position paying at least twenty-five thou-
    sand dollars annually.

## THIS WAS TOLD ME IN CONFIDENCE

Oh, I do like a little bit of gossip
In the course of a cozy little chat,
And I often wonder why
My neighbors all imply
I'm a pussy, I'm a tabby, I'm a cat.

Mrs. Dooley murmured meow at me this morning;
Mrs. Cohen would have cut me if she could;
But my feelings aren't so filmy
That names are going to kill me,
And a little bit of gossip does me good.

Oh, I do like a little bit of gossip;
I am pleased with Mr. Moffet's double life.
It's provocative to watch
Mr. Taylor guzzle Scotch;
I wonder if he knows about his wife?
The sheriff wants a word with Mrs. Walker;
She doesn't pay her bills the way she should;
Yet I hear from several sources
That she gambles on the horses —
Oh, a little bit of gossip does me good.

Oh, I do like a little bit of gossip;
It seems to lend a savor to my tea;
The deplorable mistakes
That everybody makes
Are calories and vitamins to me.
If I tell you Mrs. Drew is off to Reno,
You are not to breathe a word, that's understood;
For I said to Mrs. Drew
That I heard it all from you —
Oh, a little bit of gossip does me good.

Oh, I do like a little bit of gossip,
But for scandal or for spite there's no excuse;
To think of Mrs. Page
Telling lies about my age!

Well, her tongue is like her morals, rather loose.
Mrs. Murgatroyd eats opium for breakfast,
And claims I'm running after Mr. Wood;
That sort of vicious slander
Arouses all my dander —
But a little bit of gossip does me good.


### WHEN THE DEVIL WAS SICK COULD HE PROVE IT?

Few things are duller
Than feeling unspecifically off-color,
Yes, you feel like the fulfilment of a dismal prophecy,
And you don't feel either exercisey or officey,
But still you can't produce a red throat or a white tongue
   or uneasy respiration or any kind of a symptom,
And it is very embarrassing that whoever was supposed to
   be passing out the symptoms skympom,
Because whatever is the matter with you, you can't spot it
But whatever it is, you've got it,
But the question is how to prove it,
And you suck for hours on the mercury of the thermometer
   you finally sent out for and you can't move it,
And your entire system may be pneumococci'd or strepto-
   cocci'd,
But the looks you get from your loved ones are simply
   skepticocci'd,
And Conscience glares at you in her Here comes that bad
   penny way,
Crying There's nothing the matter with you, you're just
   trying to get out of doing something you never wanted
   to do anyway,

So you unfinger your pulse before Conscience can jeer at
     you for a fingerer,
And you begin to believe that perhaps she is right, perhaps
     you are nothing but a hypochondriacal old malingerer,
And you take a farewell look at the thermometer,
And that's when you hurl the bometer.
Yes sir, it's as good as a tonic,
Because you've got as pretty a ninety-nine point one as
     you'd wish to see in a month of bubonic.
Some people hold out for a hundred or more before they
     collapse
But that leaves too many gaps;
As for me,
I can get a very smug Monday, Tuesday, Wednesday,
     Thursday, or Friday in bed out of a tenth of a degree.
It is to this trait that I am debtor
For the happy fact that on week ends I generally feel better.


## THE LAST ROLL OF SIR RALPH THE ROLLER

Sir Ralph the Roller rolled his hoop,
He rolled it into the mayor's soup.
The mayor roared, and the bells were tolling,
But Ralph the Roller kept on rolling.
The King and Queen he happened to meet,
And he rolled it over the royal feet,
When the King fell down with a cry of Lummy!
He rolled it over the royal tummy.

Oh I am Ralph the Roller!
I am a biggety bowler!

I can ride a horse, I can ride a bike,
And I'll roll my hoop wherever I like!
Go catch a wolf, catch a bear,
Catch an elephant, if you dare,
Catch a bird or a bumble bee,
But now or never, you won't catch me!

Sir Ralph the Roller rolled his hoop,
He rolled it over the chicken coop.
The farmer fussed, and roared disaster,
But Ralph the Roller rolled the faster.
Into the kitchen and over the cook,
Through the yard and across the brook,
And over a band of robbers bold,
Sir Ralph the Roller rolled and rolled.

Oh I am Ralph the Roller!
I am a biggety bowler!
I can fly like a bird and swim like a fish,
I'll roll my hoop wherever I wish!
Go catch an elf, catch a gnome,
Catch a giant and take him home,
Or a mermaid out of the magic sea,
But now or never you won't catch me!

Oh, what a furious, curious troop
Ran after Ralph and his rolling hoop!
The mayor ran, and the King and Queen,
In their flowing robes of gold and green;
The chickens ran, and the cook and the farmer,
And all the robbers in rusty armor.
Some ran threatening, some cajoling,
But Ralph the Roller kept on rolling.

Oh I am Ralph the Roller!
I am a biggety bowler!
I can tread a dance, I can whistle a tune,
I can roll my hoop around the moon!
Go catch the smoke, catch the spark,
Catch the shadows after dark,
Catch the wind in the willow tree,
But now or never, you won't catch me!

Sir Ralph the Roller gave a whoop,
And into the sky he rolled his hoop.
He rolled it over the King's balloon,
And he broke his hoop, so he rolled the moon.
And east, and west, and north, and south,
The people stared with open mouth,
And all agreed that Ralph the Roller
Was a most especially biggety bowler.

## TELL IT TO THE ESKIMOS
### or
## TELL IT TO THE ESQUIMAUX

Ethelbert Jukes is full of health,
And he doesn't care who knows it.
Others may exercise by stealth,
But he with a cry of *Prosit!*
Others put up with coated tongues,
And shoulders narrow and droopy;
Ethelbert overinflates his lungs
With a thundering shout of Whoopee!
Ethelbert's noise is healthy noise,
Ethelbert's joys are healthy joys,

[ 135 ]

Ethelbert shunts the primrose path,
And starts the day with an icy bath.

I might forgive the super-physique
Contained in the Jukes apparel;
The apple glowing in either cheek;
The chest like an oyster barrel;
The muscles that flow like a mountain stream,
The result of applied eugenics;
The rigorous diet, the stern régime
Of arduous calisthenics;
I can pardon most of the healthy joys,
I can pardon most of the healthy noise,
But Heaven itself no pardon hath
For the man who boasts of an icy bath.

If the Missing Links were vigorous chaps
And their manly deeds were myriad,
Must civilization then relapse
Back to the glacial period?
Humanity learns at a fearful price;
Must the lessons all be lost?
Does the locomotive feed on ice?
Is the liner propelled by frost?

One constant truth mankind has found
Through fire and flood and slaughter:
The thing that makes the wheels go round
Is plenty of good hot water.
And therefore, therefore, Ethelbert Jukes,
You deserve the harshest of harsh rebukes;

Ogden Nash.

## THE BIRDS

Puccini was Latin and Wagner Teutonic,
And birds are incurably philharmonic.
Suburban yards and rural vistas
Are filled with avian Andrews Sisters.
The skylark sings a roundelay,
The crow sings "The Road to Mandalay,"
The nightingale sings a lullaby
And the sea gull sings a gullaby.
That's what shepherds listened to in Arcadia
Before somebody invented the radia.

You and your frigid daily bath
Are blocking civilization's path.
And since cold water won't lather, Bertie,
Permit me to add that your neck is dirty.